LIFE NATURE LIBRARY

THE
MOUNTAINS

TIME
LIFE
BOOKS
®

LIFE WORLD LIBRARY

LIFE NATURE LIBRARY

TIME READING PROGRAM

THE LIFE HISTORY OF THE UNITED STATES

LIFE SCIENCE LIBRARY

INTERNATIONAL BOOK SOCIETY

GREAT AGES OF MAN

TIME-LIFE LIBRARY OF ART

TIME-LIFE LIBRARY OF AMERICA

FOODS OF THE WORLD

LIFE NATURE LIBRARY

THE MOUNTAINS

by Lorus J. Milne and Margery Milne
and the Editors of
TIME-LIFE BOOKS

TIME-LIFE BOOKS   NEW YORK

About the Authors

Lorus J. Milne and Margery Milne have acquired their knowledge of the earth and its wildlife from personal observation on field
trips covering more than 363,000 miles all over the globe. They
met at Harvard, where Canadian-born Lorus Milne had come to
take a Ph.D. in biology. Mrs. Milne was studying for her Ph.D. in
the same science. Dr. Milne is now on the faculty of the University
of New Hampshire, where Mrs. Milne has also taught. They have
lectured extensively and have written for *The Atlantic Monthly*,
The American Scholar, *Audubon Magazine*, *Natural History* and
Scientific American. Their books have been translated into several
languages and include *The Balance of Nature*, *Plant Life*, *Animal
Life*, *Paths Across the Earth*, *The World of Night*, *The Mating In-
stinct*, *The Biotic World and Man* and *A Multitude of Living Things*.

ON THE COVER: Clinging to the
slopes at timber line beneath the
snowy peak of Mount Baker in
Washington are straggling lines
of fir and patches of huckleberry
and frost-tinted mountain maple.

Contents

TIME-LIFE BOOKS

EDITOR
Maitland A. Edey
EXECUTIVE EDITOR
Jerry Korn
TEXT DIRECTOR   ART DIRECTOR
Martin Mann   Sheldon Cotler
CHIEF OF RESEARCH
Beatrice T. Dobie
PICTURE EDITOR
Robert G. Mason
Assistant Text Directors:
Harold C. Field, Ogden Tanner
Assistant Art Director: Arnold C. Holeywell
Assistant Chief of Research: Martha Turner

•

PUBLISHER
Rhett Austell
Associate Publisher: Walter C. Rohrer
General Manager: Joseph C. Hazen Jr.
Planning Director: John P. Sousa III
Circulation Director: Joan D. Manley
Marketing Director: Carter Smith
Business Manager: John D. McSweeney
Publishing Board: Nicholas Benton, Louis Bronzo,
James Wendell Forbes

LIFE NATURE LIBRARY

EDITOR: Maitland A. Edey
Associate Editor: Richard L. Williams
Assistants to the Editor: George McCue, John Paul Porter
Designer: Paul Jensen
Staff Writers: Hubert Kay, John MacDonald, Paul W. Schwartz,
Gerald Simons, Carl Solberg, David S. Thomson
Chief Researcher: Martha Turner
Researchers: Susan Bremer, Doris Bry, Peggy Bushong, Joan Chasin,
Nelson J. Darrow, Eleanor Feltser, Paula Norworth,
Roxanna Sayre, Victor H. Waldrop, Phyllis M. Williamson

EDITORIAL PRODUCTION
Color Director: Robert L. Young
Copy Staff: Marian Gordon Goldman, Suzanne Seixas,
Florence Keith
Picture Department: Dolores A. Littles, Joan T. Lynch
Art Assistants: James D. Smith, Mark A. Binn

The text for the chapters of this book was written by Lorus and Margery Milne, the text for the picture essays by the editorial staff. The following individuals and departments of Time Inc. were helpful in producing the book: LIFE staff photographers Eliot Elisofon, Dmitri Kessel and George Silk; Editorial Production, Robert W. Boyd Jr.; Editorial Reference, Peter Draz; Picture Collection, Doris O'Neil; Photographic Laboratory, George Karas; TIME-LIFE News Service, Richard M. Clurman.

Introduction

AORANGI, icy pyramid above the Tasman Glacier; emerald green Matafao against white trade-wind clouds and the deep blue Samoan sea; the Rockies shining ahead over the prairie—the mountains on the horizon always attract and challenge.

Man is drawn to mountains for many reasons: economic, scientific, aesthetic, and for just plain adventure. Here are those last bits of wilderness so necessary for the occasional escape from the pressures of modern life. The magnificent photographs and informative text in this new addition to the LIFE Nature Library convey all the beauty and freshness of the mountain wilderness. They will inspire in us all a greater appreciation of our mountain landscapes.

Mountains come in all shapes, sizes and climates—the typically snowy alpine peaks with clear air and flowered meadows, the cloudy and ferny green tropical mountains dripping with water, and the sharp, dry mountains of the desert. But they all have one thing in common: they are colder on top than on the lower slopes. Thus they are a testing ground of evolution toward cold-tolerance. For it is in the mountains that one most readily sees how plants and animals have managed to become adapted to severe environmental conditions of all kinds. Most life survives easily in the warm lowlands. But one by one each kind reaches its upper limit on the mountainside. The fine forests of the lower slopes give way to the twisted and sprawling trees of the timber line, and the alpine meadows to the almost inorganic world of the ice peaks.

Only a relative handful of species has solved the problems of growth and reproduction during the short alpine summer. Here, life of tropical origin faces its severest test. Through millions of years, new forms from the valleys and slopes invade the highlands, and only the successful few pass through the environmental sifting. During colder periods in the earth's history, these alpine species migrate along the great cordilleras and across the lowland gaps to enrich the biota of other mountain ranges, and eventually of the polar regions themselves. But during the long warm swings of the climatic cycle, the alpine summits are like islands in the sky, providing isolation for speciation.

The mountains were already old when man appeared, and yet they hold the challenge and the opportunity of the future. Let us enjoy them wisely. This book will provide an introduction for those who have yet to see a mountain or feel the bright sun and cold winds of the high country—and it will be a source of new information and added pleasure for those who have long known the mountains as home.

WILLIAM DWIGHT BILLINGS
Professor of Botany
Duke University
Durham, North Carolina

1

The Earth
and Its Heights

OF the many astonishing things about mountains, perhaps the most astonishing is that they exist at all. Why should they? They were not
there when the earth was young, and they may not be when it is old.
When the globe's pulse runs down, when its fires cool and its oceans freeze,
the eternal peaks may be gone. If anything mountainlike remains, it may
be nothing more than some worn-down nubs, and it is certain that these
will not be the remnants of mountains we know today. They will be their
grandchildren—five, 10, perhaps 20 generations removed from the Rockies,
the Alps and Himalayas, which are the present so-called "young" gen-
eration of mountains. Where their descendants, the dim crags of the
future, will rise, no one knows.

All that is certain is that mountains have risen, under the urging of
forces deep within the earth, in a continuing succession since the first
granite peak appeared some three billion years ago, and they will undoubtedly continue to do so for at least as long in the future. The life of a
mountain is like that of a patriarch among men. It is born, it has a vigorous
youth, a long maturity, an even longer old age, and finally it is worn down

into the earth and disappears. These processes take time, but time is in full supply in the universe; a million years in the life of the earth is like a few days in the life of a man. And in proportion to the total bulk of the terrestrial body from which it springs, a mountain is about the size of a very small pimple on the back of a human neck—and, again in proportion, it endures about as long.

This knowledge of mountains is relatively new. For as long as man has thought about them at all, the hills have seemed ageless, simply a part of the larger marvelous act of creation for which every society, every faith, has had its own explanation. Only 200 years ago that most rational and skeptical of men, Voltaire, regarded as preposterous the view held by a scientist friend of his, the Comte de Buffon, that even the small eminences in France might not always have been there. Buffon had become fascinated by sea shells he had discovered imbedded in rocks on the hillsides of France. How had they gotten there? After studying them he gradually became convinced that sea animals had once lived at the places where the mountains now stood. He suggested that soft sediments had covered them and hardened into rocks in shallow seas, and that later the rocks had been lifted high above sea level. Nonsense, said Voltaire; pilgrims from the seashore carried the shells to the mountaintop and left them to be mired in mud after rain. The two men argued the point and their friendship cooled.

IN Buffon's day the science of geology was in its infancy and the theory of evolution was still a hundred years away. Even so, scientists of the time had a remarkably precise understanding of the solar system. They knew within an error of 4 or 5 per cent the earth's size. They had determined, with comparable accuracy, its distance from the sun, the length of its year, the size and nature of the moon, and the behavior of most of the planets. Thanks to Isaac Newton, they even had an explanation for the force that held the whole system together. They knew a good deal less about the earth under their feet. Nathaniel Hawthorne, a century ago, still had no idea that he was taking poetic license when he wrote that "mountains are earth's undecaying monuments."

But digging and sifting and comparing has been going on at an ever-increasing rate. The mountains themselves offer endless clues to their own origin simply because they project so high and expose so many layers of interesting rock and peculiar fossils for study. The idea that they spring up and die like toadstools is no longer derided. The evidence is all around us that they do. We can see them wearing away before our eyes, the irreversible forces of erosion and gravity remorselessly leveling them as fast as they are thrust up. We have learned that there are four major ways in which mountains can be built. We are beginning to understand that the shifting of great weights of rock and sand toward the oceans creates instabilities in the earth's crust which provide the impetus for further mountain-building in other places. We suspect, too, that all mountains are supported by "upside-down" mountains penetrating deep into the earth. In short, much is known of *what* happens. *How* and *why* are more complex questions and will be discussed in the next chapter.

Meanwhile, rising or falling, mountains are something to conjure with. Every continent has them and probably always has had them, although not in the same places where they are found now. How fast they rise and fall varies, of course, with time and location. Almost nothing is known of this at present because accurate measuring devices are of very recent invention, and there simply has not been enough time for most mountains (except volcanoes) to change their heights sufficiently for man to record the differences. Mountain peaks in Norway and Sweden now appear to be growing at a rate of about two feet a century. This is because the entire Scandinavian Peninsula, relieved of the crushing weight of the glaciers which covered it during the last ice age, is rising. Mount Everest, which was first measured "accurately" by a British survey in 1852, proved to be 29,002 feet high. This, as every schoolboy knows, is the highest point on earth. But it turned out to be 26 feet higher when again measured in 1954 by a party of Indians. Had it risen that much in a hundred years? This is hard to say, since mountain-measuring, even with the best instruments, is not easy. As the mountain expert Ferdinand Lane explains it, measurements must be made optically through a delicate surveying transit which can be accurate only if its base is absolutely level. This may be achieved by using a spirit level or a plumb bob, but neither device can be trusted fully because the great mass of the mountain itself has a gravitational attraction which may pull the bob off line by a tiny but significant amount. Furthermore, the earth is not exactly round, being thicker through the equator than through the poles by a matter of nearly 27 miles, and this too must be taken into account. Finally, the atmosphere itself plays some fancy tricks with light rays. Morning measurements taken of Dhaulagiri from a single point in the Himalayas varied by as much as 500 feet from those taken that same afternoon.

Thus, every recorded measurement of a large mountain may be from half a dozen to a few hundred feet in error. The point is emphasized by the way the first "official" height of Everest was arrived at. Measurements were made from six places. All were different, the lowest being 28,990 feet and the highest 29,026 feet. When all six were averaged, the figure came to exactly 29,000 feet. Unwilling to publish what they thought would seem like an estimate rather than an exact figure, the surveyors arbitrarily added two feet to make the official figure sound better.

WHATEVER its exact height, Everest is still the highest mountain. There is no known spot on earth today which is higher, although persistent sightings of a peak of nearly 30,000 feet in western China were reported by fliers during World War II. This mountain is named Amne Machin and is now known to be in an area of peaks that reach 25,000 feet. Whether Everest will remain the highest is quite another matter. In time, of course, it will wear away and be outtopped by mountains as yet unborn. How high they will rise is unpredictable. There is no presently known limit to the height to which a mass of rock may be thrust, and a peak of 35,000 or even 40,000 feet is entirely possible. Indeed, peaks of this grandeur may already have existed more than once in the past.

Height itself is relative: what constitutes a mountain depends on who is looking at it and how big the surrounding eminences are. Thus the Watchung mountains in New Jersey are a mere 400 to 500 feet high, whereas some 12,000-foot shafts in the Himalayas, which Lane once asked his Tibetan guide to identify, were shrugged off as being mere foothills, so insignificant that no one had ever bothered to give them names. Ignoring for a moment Webster's definition ("any part of a land mass which projects conspicuously above its surroundings"), a good idea of the really lofty areas of the earth may be gained by arbitrarily choosing some respectable figure, say 3,000 feet, and figuratively flooding the planet that deep in water to see what still projects above the surface. The result is shown in the painting on pages 44 and 45 in this book, and it reveals a most interesting fact. With a few exceptions, the world's mountains run in broad belts, or cordilleras. In the Western Hemisphere, the cordilleras run like a backbone from Alaska to Tierra del Fuego. The North American cordillera, which continues into the Andean cordillera of South America, includes the Coast Ranges, Sierra Nevada-Cascade, Great Basin and Rocky Mountain systems in the United States. The cordilleras of Eurasia are more complex, with three belts radiating out from a central point in the Pamir mountains of the south-central Soviet Union. One of these belts extends westward through Asia Minor, southern Europe and the Atlas system of North Africa. Another, which includes the Himalayas, radiates southeast from the Pamirs through Asia, the East Indies, Australia and New Zealand. The third belt runs northeastward to the Bering Strait to connect with the North American cordillera. In Africa, high areas in the east along the Great Rift Valley zone, though impressive, are not considered a major cordillera, either in structure or in surface form. Other mountain ranges which occur outside these major belts are insignificant by comparison.

Over a quarter of the earth's present 56-million-square-mile land surface is more than 3,000 feet high. Tibet, whose boundaries are entirely contained within mountainous regions, has an *average* altitude of about 15,000 feet, which outtops all but the six tallest peaks in Europe and all but three in the continental United States, and these are in Alaska.

M OUNTAINS have had a profound effect on the earth and on the history of all life. To begin with, they provide the raw materials for the soil. The early surface of the planet, as it hardened into continents, was probably light granitic rock. The best way for this material to be crumbled was for it to be upthrust high enough so that bits of it could break off under the influence of water and wind. For water to fall, for it to work as an erosive force, there must be something like a mountainside for it to tumble down, a stream bed or a canyon in which it can carry smaller rocks and grind them to sand and dust. At the same time, these forces work hand in hand with chemical and frost erosion, and even the direct but minute action of raindrops themselves.

The tiny particles thus created made up the fine, loose materials into which primitive plants, emerging from the sea, could extend their filaments. They provided surfaces and crannies into which myriads of bacteria and small organisms could penetrate and die, slowly enriching the sterile material with the remains of their own bodies and creating the soil which gradually made the landward invasion from the sea by both plants and animals an increasingly rapid process. If the dry surfaces of the earth had remained solid rock, little life would exist on land today. Never could life have developed the richness and variety that it now possesses. Man would not be here at all.

Mountains have affected the course of life in other ways. They have a powerful influence on weather since they break up the orderly flow of winds

HOW PLANTS ADAPT to different environments is shown by these three yarrows, once identical but now evolving into distinct species. The first, taken from sea level, has a nine-month growing season and must produce a tall stem and large leaves to compete with other fast-growing plants. The second, taken from 5,000 feet, with a shorter growing season, wastes less energy on stem and leaves. The third, from 11,000 feet, can grow for only 65 days and can afford only a six-inch stem and tiny leaves. These characteristics are now set in all three plants: each will follow its own pattern wherever it is planted.

around the earth, creating local eddies which in turn affect temperature and rainfall and are responsible for a wide spectrum of climates, not only in the immediate vicinity of the mountains themselves but sometimes in areas thousands of miles away. The grand scheme of climate on the earth would be a simple affair if there were no mountains or continents to interfere with the majestic flow of wind and water set up by heat differences and by the rotation of the globe. Under these influences the prevailing direction of winds in temperate latitudes is from the west. In the United States they blow steadily against the coasts of Washington, Oregon and California, carrying a full load of moisture from the Pacific. At once they encounter the coastal mountain ranges. They are pushed upward, growing colder as they rise. Their moisture condenses into rain and falls on the western slopes of the mountains, this precipitation running as high as 12 feet a year in the Olympic rain forest of Washington. Wrung dry, the winds pass on over the mountains, whose eastern slopes get scarcely any rain at all. Because of mountains the driest deserts in America are separated from some of its greenest areas by only one or two hundred miles.

CLIMBING a mountain, one is immediately struck by the fact that the higher one goes the colder it gets. This is certainly true, but it does not seem right since one is approaching closer and closer to the sun. The explanation lies in the fact that the air is drier, and thus holds less of the warming infrared rays of the sun. The result is a lowering of average temperature by about three degrees Fahrenheit for every 1,000 feet of altitude. Nevertheless, as skiers and climbers know, the sun blisters the skin at high altitudes although little heat is felt. This is because the blistering ultraviolet rays are filtered out less by the dry atmosphere.

By combining differences in rainfall with differences in temperature, a single mountain range can produce a bewildering variety of climates, and thus have a profound influence on the evolution of plants and animals. There is a tendency in evolution, known as natural selection, for slight differences among individuals in a population to be perpetuated, if the differences are advantageous. For example, smaller members of a warm-blooded species have a harder time than larger ones in keeping warm in cold climates because the ratio of their skin surface (by which body heat is lost) to total body weight is greater. Song sparrows, which are common all over North America, demonstrate this very well, since the races found in Alaska are measurably larger than those found in arid areas of the Southwest. In the desert small size is an advantage, helping the birds keep cool. A similar principle plainly operates on steep mountainsides, where extremes of climate may be found within a mile or so of each other, and it results in horizontal bands of animal and plant life, each adapted to its particular altitude. Sparrows of the heights tend to keep separate from sparrows of the valleys. If this separation is continued, their genetic differences, which were very slight to begin with, become greater and greater. In a million years or so the various strains may become so different that they will no longer be able to interbreed—and new species will have been formed.

Even man, during his short stay on earth, has been influenced by mountains. If he were not so skilled at adjusting himself to various environments by the use of fire and shelter and clothing, racial differences probably would be greater than they are, for groups of men would have remained where they found themselves for longer periods of time. They would not have been able to roam the world and interbreed as they have done. Even so, there are marked differences in races today. Mongolians are unlike Caucasians in that they tend to have thicker bodies and shorter extremities. Anthropologists have speculated that these differences came about over many thousands of years during which one large group of humans found itself trapped north of the Himalayas by the ice ages.

Man today lives everywhere except in the polar regions and on the tops of the world's highest mountains. It is not the intense cold, or even the altitude, which keeps him away, but the snow. In an environment that is perpetually snow-covered, plants will not flourish, animals cannot forage, and man must seek his living elsewhere. Still, he penetrates as high as he can, and has managed to exist in remote Andean valleys and Tibetan heights where sea-level dwellers can scarcely catch their breath. Again this is made possible by biological adaptation. Mountain peoples have larger hearts than lowlanders, larger lungs and blood that is richer in red cells. Despite these adaptations, existence in the mountains is hard, and mountain men are hard themselves. They are self-reliant, by reputation individualistic and freedom-loving. Liberty was described by John Milton as "the mountain nymph."

In Switzerland, the roar of conquest has rolled repeatedly against the flanks of the Alps but the Swiss spirit of independence has persisted. They have made the most of their assets—scenery, water power and the produce of their fertile valleys. All derive directly from mountains, for the Alps catch an immense amount of rain and snow, making the valleys green, electricity plentiful and the jumbled peaks, with their gleaming snow fields and mighty glaciers, a mecca for tourists.

Snow is a mixed blessing to the Alpine dweller. It lingers late in spring, making for a short growing season. In bad years it chokes the high valleys and passes, making travel impossible. And it occasionally drops like a white shroud from the almost vertical rock walls, obliterating entire villages in immense avalanches. Snow also feeds the Swiss glaciers, which cover about 700 square miles of the country's precious land, creeping down the flanks of the mountains, scouring the rocks and, where the ice melts, leaving long hills of stones and gravel. Swiss scientists were the first in the world to study the habits of glaciers and to conclude that they are but the remains of much larger ice sheets that covered northern Europe some 12,000 years ago. From studies of terminal moraines (heaps of earth and gravel) in areas where no glaciers are today, from parallel scratches in rocks and from the presence of huge boulders hundreds of miles from where they belonged, it became clear that ice had been there and had left

PROFILE OF A GLACIER shows its principal segments. The crack, or bergschrund, at top, occurs where a downward movement pulls the ice away from snow clinging to the mountainside. Farther down, it splits into crevasses created by movement over rough ground at varying speeds within the glacier itself.

Debris, dislodged from the flanks or scraped up from the bottom, is deposited in piles, or moraines, at the melting edge of the mass of ice. A glacial staircase is created as chunks of rock are quarried out of fractured areas. A cirque, swept clean by continuous movement, may turn into a lake, or tarn, after the ice has melted.

BERGSCHRUND

ICEFALL

CIRQUE

GLACIAL STAIRCASE

MORAINES

debris behind. Present estimates indicate that the glacial cap in the Alps may have been as much as a mile deep, which means that only the tops of the highest mountains projected above it, and that the rest of the country was drowned under trillions of tons of solid ice—every one of today's green valleys filled to the brim like a cup.

During historic times the Alpine glaciers have been in constant fluctuation, but always within limits close to their present sizes. In the last century they have shrunk fairly steadily, in concert with almost all the world's glaciers. But in the past decade glaciers in some parts of the world have begun to grow again.

A glacier's growth depends on the delicate balance between temperature and snowfall. If more snow is deposited on it than can evaporate or melt away in summer, it will grow. Otherwise it will shrink. A glacier contains three main sections, all smoothly connected: the snow field at the source, called the area of accumulation; the glacier body itself; and the terminus, its lower end. These areas are not constant, of course. One part slowly becomes another, since the entire mass is in continual movement, flowing ever downward like very cold, very hard molasses.

Fresh snow falling on the upper slopes of a glacier is turned to ice in a regular process. Snowflakes, being star-shaped and light, collect in a fluffy mass at first, with much air between them. Changes in the weather subject them to evaporation and melting; their delicate points are the first to disappear, and they become rounded grains of snow about a twentieth of an inch in diameter. A boring made near the top of a glacier will reveal that the deeper one drills, the rounder and more closely packed the grains will be. These tiny snow granules are known as névé and are usually at least a year old. Further packing and the dripping of melt-water down between the grains gradually turns them to particles of ice. These slowly merge with one another, growing larger and larger until at a depth of 50 or 60 feet they may be as much as half an inch across. At this depth, surface conditions no longer affect them and they respond only to pressure from the weight of the material above them. When they are 100 feet down they are usually compressed into solid ice. In warm climates, where there is much melting, the transformation from snowflakes to névé to ice may take from one to 20 years. In very cold climates it may take as long as 300 years.

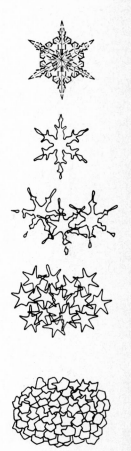

BREAKDOWN OF SNOWFLAKES into ice follows a fixed process within a glacier. Evaporation and melting gradually change star-shaped flakes (top) into small snow granules (center). These condense into a mass of icy particles (bottom) which, when further packed down, becomes solid ice.

THE speed at which valley glacial ice may move depends on the steepness of the slope on which it lies, the depth of the ice, and the load of ice and snow at its source. Some glaciers on gradual slopes, and where there is little build-up of snow to add weight up above and urge them along, move outward at their terminus at a speed of less than half an inch a day. Others, on steep slopes and burdened with much new snow, may move as much as 100 feet a day. Continental glaciers like the Greenland ice sheet, as they spread gradually outward, can even flow uphill, covering entire ranges, sometimes leaving exposed peaks called nunataks.

Movement is by no means uniform within a glacier, as men who dig tunnels into them have discovered. The tunnels rapidly bend and must be constantly re-hewn if they are to be kept open. From such experiments it has been learned that the flow in the center of a glacier is more rapid than that along the "shore," much as in a river, whose banks exert a drag on the flow of water. Also, the deeper one goes in a glacier, the slower the movement. Among the first to penetrate to the bottom of a large glacier was a group of Soviet scientists from the Academy of Sciences of the Kazakh S.S.R., which sent an expedition to the Zailisky glacier in the northern Tien Shan mountains. The party lowered a string of electrodes into a hole 172 feet to the bottom of the glacier, then froze the electrodes in place by filling the hole with water. The varying rates of advance at different levels were determined by locating each electrode by means of the electric field it produced. Over a period of 190 days, the surface of the glacier moved 7.5 feet, while the base moved along only five feet, with a gradual transition in between.

Because of different rates of travel within a glacier, large cracks appear in its lower sections and at points where the slope abruptly drops. These are known as crevasses. They can be as narrow as a few inches or more than 45 feet across, and some have been measured that are more than 120 feet deep. Seasoned mountaineers have difficulty spotting crevasses when the surfaces are covered with fresh snow and to the inexperienced they are a constant menace. Since glaciers have been studied so intensively in the Alps and their rates of movement so precisely calculated, this has led to a ghoulish kind of arithmetic: when will the body of an entombed man reappear at the melting face at the bottom of a glacier? In 1820 three climbers fell into a crevasse on a Mont Blanc glacier. It was calculated that their bodies would reappear in 1860. They did so in 1861. In the summer of 1956 a glacier at the foot of the Weisshorn ejected the perfectly preserved body of a man who at first was believed to be a Swiss who had fallen to the surface of the glacier from a cliff in 1946. Later, however, the body was correctly identified as that of a 19-year-old German climber, Georges Winkler, who had fallen from the Weisshorn in 1888. It had taken 68 years for the ice to carry Winkler's corpse approximately one mile from the upper glacier to its terminus.

ALL Swiss glaciers belong to the category of "valley glaciers" in contrast to the larger, more static "ice-sheet" commonly found in polar regions, and of which the continental glaciers of Greenland and Antarctica are the finest examples. The Antarctic continent, being studded with high mountains, has both types, which combine to make up the largest conglomerate ice cake in the world—five million square miles in area and of unknown thickness in most of its parts.

By contrast, Switzerland's glaciers are puny, the best-known being the Rhone glacier, some eight miles long. Nevertheless, they are impressive. The Rhone glacier is the source of the Rhone river, which has the largest volume of any river in France. Though it is presently shrinking, the glacier constitutes an ever-present menace to those who live in the valley nearest to its terminus. For if Switzerland's climate should turn only a few degrees colder, the Rhone glacier would march downward, obliterating nearly 30 towns and villages, including Sion, a city of over 12,000 inhabitants, before it even reached Lake Geneva. Simultaneously, glaciers would shoulder their way into all the other mountain valleys, an eventuality which underscores the small margin of safety under which a mountain society operates. With only a slight but prolonged change in its climate, Switzerland would become uninhabitable.

COWLED IN SNOW, A SWISS ALPINE VALLEY SHELTERS A CLUSTER OF CHALETS BY A WHITE-ENAMELED RIVER NEAR ZERMATT

The Alpine Spectacle

Green-ribboned valleys and sharp-nosed peaks make up the world's best known mountain land: the European Alps. Geologically young, the Alpine steeps soar to over 15,000 feet, the product of slow folding of gneiss rock begun 15 million years ago. Protected by such high walls, the peoples who live in the valleys enjoy undisturbed prosperity and independence.

A FAIRY-TALE VALLEY twists around a spur of the 13,668-foot Jungfrau (*left*) in the Swiss Alps, tracing the path cut by an ice-age glacier that long ago melted away. Deep in the valley's emerald cup nests the village of Lauterbrunnen. Along its rim perch the chalets of upland farmers. In this midsummer setting, snow lingers only on the highest peaks.

Farming the Uplands

Wringing a livelihood from the soil in Alpine country is not easy. The upland farmer must contend with obstacles unknown to his lowland cousins. First among his problems is the shortage of arable land in an area completely dominated by mountains. Farmers in the Austrian Tyrol, shown here, cultivate all available ground even when it angles as sharply as the valley does at right. Such steep land is inhumanly difficult to till. Plows must be operated by two men, one to guide the horses, the other to hold the plow in the furrow so that it will not roll down the hill. All reaping

WEARING A FLOWER-BEDECKED HAT, A FARMER JOINS A PARADE IN INNSBRUCK

LIKE AN ARMY READY FOR BATTLE, ROW ON ROW OF HAY-DRYING POSTS FILL THE GREEN ZILLER VALLEY AS FAR AS THE EYE CAN

must be done by hand with sickle and scythe since it is impossible to use modern machinery. Poor soil and a short growing season compound the farmers' problems.

Grass and clover, however, grow well in this hard environment, and as a result most Alpine farmers are primarily dairymen. Inbreeding has developed unique types of cattle, adjusted to the varied pasturage, sprier animals for the steep slopes, heavier ones for the valleys. Dairy methods have been adapted to the terrain. Pipelines up to three miles long carry milk from high farms to transfer points below in the valleys.

THE HIGH SIDES OF A STEEP VALLEY NEAR RANGGEN ARE HEAVILY CULTIVATED

SEE. TYROLEAN FARMERS PILE THEIR MOWINGS THIS WAY TO HASTEN THEIR CURING BY EXPOSING MORE OF THE HAY TO THE SUN

OUT OF A MOUNTAIN onto a bridge, a train follows the breathtaking route of Switzerland's famed Rhaetian railway. In 150 miles of track it has 376 bridges and 76 tunnels.

Getting About in the Alps

Journeying in Switzerland presents the traveler with unusual problems. Crisscrossed by mountains which rise as high as 15,000 feet and valleys that drop to 500 feet above sea level, this Alpine land is a place where, in getting from one point to another, one may have to travel the greater part of the distance straight up and down. In the past the mountains often kept the people of the cantons isolated from each other. Today accelerated building of roads, funiculars, cable cars, bridges and tunnels has helped to ease this problem of intercommunication.

The greatest aid to travel in Switzerland has been the construction of an all-electric railway network. Densest of its kind in the world, it links every canton of Switzerland. Run by hydroelectric power, the trains speed along 15,000 miles of track at clips of 100 miles per hour and more. So swift are they that their passengers complain they cannot see enough of the land's most spectacular product: its mountain scenery.

ZIGZAG ROAD to tiny villages among terraced fields on the steep southern slopes of the Alps (*opposite*) is still the farmers' daily path between their homes and the valley market.

SKY-HIGH CABLE CARS ferry passengers over the French-Italian border to the top of the 12,605-foot Aiguille du Midi. The line, one of the longest in the Alps, extends three miles.

A COTTONY PLAIN OF CLOUD smothers the green valleys of the Italian Alps in an azure mist. Caused by a layer of cool air forming over the Po River in northern Italy, the upper edge of the mist cuts off the jagged peaks at about the 6,000-foot level. The strange scene is a reminder of a similar one 12,000 years ago when Europe was in the grip

of the most recent ice age and a sheet of glacial ice covered these same valleys to a depth almost even with the top of this cloud bank. The erosive effects of the ice sheet can be seen in semicircular gouges called cirques, visible in mountains at the left of the picture. Also visible are the tops of several glaciers, remnants of the ice field itself.

Reminders of a Great Ice Age

Switzerland owes much to its glaciers. Though they encroach on its tiny land area, overspreading almost 5 per cent of the country with billions of tons of ice and snow, they are a major reason why it is habitable at all. Because of glaciers the Alps abound with fertile valleys like the one on pages 18 and 19. A million years ago, Switzerland is believed to have been a country of bare rock peaks divided by narrow, V-shaped canyons. Then the last great ice age began and four successive glacial sheets ground through these clefts, slowly but irresistibly widening and deepening them until the softly rounded valleys of today were created. Each time the ice retreated, it left the residue of its erosion behind as soil. Today the melting remnants of the glaciers serve to water the soil of the valleys, making them green for the cattle and goats of Swiss herdsmen.

A RAGGED CREVASSE pierces a glacier (*opposite*). These steep-walled cracks, sometimes 200 feet deep, can be treacherous when snow-covered. Unseen, they trap unwary skiers.

FINGERS OF ICE, remnants of a once-massive glacier, infringe on a Swiss valley near Saas-Fee. At center is a moraine, a pile of broken rock left by the ice as it melted.

27

THE START OF AN AVALANCHE on an Alpine ridge shows where the slide pulled away from an incline, leaving blocks of sheared snow behind. A widening crack in the bank

A LADDER OF FENCES up a steep Swiss mountainside prevents avalanches by holding heavy snowfalls in place on the slope. The method is expensive but has worked well.

ROARING DOWNWARD from the Giessen glacier on Switzerland's Jungfrau, an avalanche plows toward a valley below. Often accompanied by a tornadolike wind and working

above the blocks indicates how these slides begin. Jarred loose by a sudden disturbance, the snow relaxes its grip on the slope and is dragged downward by its own weight.

up speeds of 70 miles an hour, such stupendous slides sweep rocks, trees, houses irresistibly before them. They frequently occur in the Alps, and take approximately 20 lives a year.

A NARROW MISS of a huge snowslide fans out in a valley near a huddled hamlet in Switzerland. The contour of the land protects the houses and the pine forest behind them.

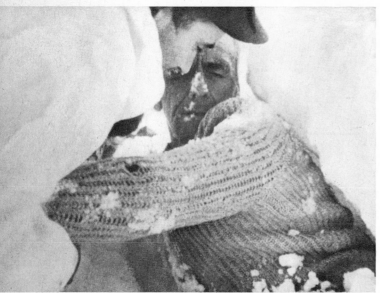

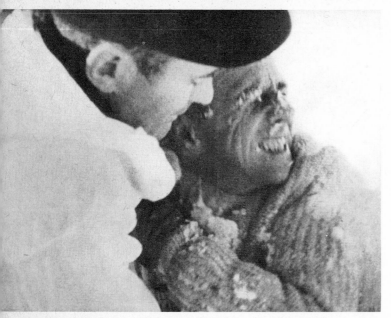

The White Death

As the Alpine winter sets in and the first snow falls, a terror returns to haunt the lives of mountain folk. It is the threat of the white death: avalanches. A hazard unique to regions of steep-sided mountains, avalanches may strike without warning, engulfing villages under millions of tons of snow. The danger varies from year to year, depending on the snowfall and the weather, but no year passes without its toll in lives. In 1951 snowslides killed nearly 400 in Switzerland alone.

Not much is needed to start an avalanche. When conditions are ripe, the slightest added weight on a slope—like a clump of snow falling off a tree—will precipitate a slide. Even a vibration—a slammed door—will suffice. When the slide is over, the grim work begins of searching for victims in its path. Men cautiously probing deep drifts with long wire poles are joined by police dogs (*left*) trained to locate people buried under seven feet of snow.

The most exasperating part of avalanches is their cruel capriciousness. In 1954, after workers had rescued survivors of a snowslide at Blons, Austria, a second slide reburied all 25 along with their rescuers. Yet a 70-year-old woman, trapped in the same slide, was recovered alive after having been under the snow for 50 hours.

BURIED ALIVE by an avalanche, a man is saved from a deep drift. After a trained dog digs down to him (*top*), he struggles to full consciousness in the arms of a rescuer (*bottom*).

STRIKING AT NIGHT, a snowslide near Vals, Switzerland, smashed this house (*opposite*), burying 19 people. Workmen dig to see if anyone may be alive under the snow.

2

Birth and Death of Mountains

IT is 200 years since Voltaire and Buffon had their famous disagreement about how sea shells found their way to mountaintops. And while it seems painfully obvious today that Buffon knew what he was talking about and Voltaire did not, it was certainly not so clear then. Voltaire believed in facts and reason, and he saw no reason to believe that mountains were anything but static. However, his political views obliged him to leave his native France from time to time for the freer air of Switzerland. There, surrounded by the upthrusting and eroding evidence of the peaks themselves, he was reminded daily of Buffon's arguments. Eventually he accepted them, and the two men became friends again.

This episode clearly shows man's natural tendency to believe that our earth today is exactly as it always has been. What power could have raised the land and shaped it into a mountain? It is far easier to comprehend the forces that work to destroy a splendid peak than it is to understand how its immense mass of rock was thrust upward in the first place. The forces that do the work lie concealed deep within the earth and man must direct his attention to those dark depths to find out how mountains are born.

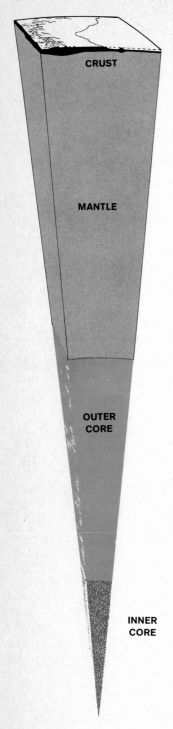

CRUST

MANTLE

OUTER CORE

INNER CORE

A SLICE OF EARTH shows its layers as deduced by scientists. The rocky crust, rarely over 40 miles thick, is here drawn at twice its actual scale. Deeper layers are in correct scale. The plastic mantle underneath the crust is the widest layer, extending for 1,800 miles. The outer core, of molten nickel-iron, is 1,300 miles thick. The dense inner core, of nickel-iron compressed solid, has a radius of 860 miles.

This is a very difficult inquiry, for man has never been able to penetrate more than a tiny fraction of the earth's crust. This crust, furthermore, is only a tiny fraction of the earth, a thin layer of rock rarely more than 40 miles thick. It bears about the same relationship to the total bulk of the earth that the shell of an egg bears to the egg. Underneath the earth's crust is a much thicker middle layer called the "mantle," which extends to a depth of about 1,800 miles, where it is replaced by the "core," a ball-shaped mass of very hot, very dense liquid believed to be molten nickel-iron. The latest studies indicate that the very center of this molten core may be solid. There is no direct proof of this picture of the structure of the earth, but a good deal of indirect and extremely ingenious evidence has been assembled in recent years.

To begin with, man has never succeeded in drilling even to the bottom of the surface crust. The deepest mine in the world goes down a mere two miles—only about a twentieth of the way—and from it we have learned one thing: the deeper one goes, the hotter it gets. Other mines all over the world exhibit the same characteristic. From a study of this evidence, it is not hard to calculate that the rock temperature rises at a fairly regular rate: one degree for every 60 feet of depth. At about three miles it is hot enough to boil water, which is proved by the action of geysers.

A third proof that the interior of the earth is hot is found in the action of volcanoes. When a volcano erupts, it sends out glowing cinders, fiery gases and molten streams of rock that flow like molasses. Clearly, it is *very* hot down where the volcanic material comes from. How far down this is cannot be measured directly, and it is tempting to assume that the earth is the same all the way to the center, just hotter and hotter, with the solid rock gradually becoming molten rock. That this is not so was discovered by a Yugoslavian scientist named A. Mohorovičić, who spent a lifetime observing earthquakes. An earthquake is a shock wave. Touch a bowl of jelly, and the whole thing will jiggle. In fact, if the properties of the jelly are known, it will be possible to predict exactly *how* it will jiggle, for shock waves behave in different ways in different materials. Thus, a convulsion of some sort deep in the ground may set up a shock wave which will travel all over the earth, and seismometers (the delicate instruments made to measure earthquakes) will jiggle in tune to the movement of the wave from one hemisphere to another. By making precise observations of the different times that a particular shock wave hits their particular instruments, seismologists in different parts of the world can compare notes and figure out exactly where an earthquake started.

The odd thing about seismology was that occasionally there were shock waves that did not behave as expected. They moved from place to place either too fast or too slowly. Even more puzzling, some of them seemed never to reach certain parts of the world at all. It was as though a barrier stood in the way, buried in the earth, the result being that a quake in Australia, say, would not be recorded in England; England clearly lay in the shadow of something deep and unseen. From long study of these inconsistencies, Professor Mohorovičić and others deduced that shock waves were passing through, or around, materials of different natures, and the present picture of the earth—a thin crust, a doughlike layer of mantle and a molten core with a solid center—began to emerge. Today a vast amount of earthquake evidence has been assembled and it supports the picture so precisely that most scientists regard it as correct. To honor the professor's work, the zone, about 40 miles down, where crust ends and mantle begins, and where shock waves bend, has been named the Mohorovičić discontinuity—or Moho, for short.

What has all this to do with mountain-building? Simply this—that if the picture of a malleable underbody beneath the earth's crust is acceptable, it then becomes possible to speculate how the crust may behave. To take a homely example, if the center of a pillow is punched, the sides will bulge up. Similarly, if a spot on the earth's surface receives an immense punch, there is bound to be a compensating bulging-up somewhere else.

The punches that the earth receives are incredibly slow and gentle. They take millions of years to make themselves felt, and the best place to observe them is at the mouths of great rivers. Rivers carry silt into the sea constantly. Fine mud slowly packs down and hardens into shale. Coarse sand becomes consolidated into vast layers of sandstone. Limy remains of plants and animals are turned into limestone rock. Layer after layer builds up. It has been estimated that a vigorous river can discharge enough mud to build a foot of shale in a century. An equal thickness of limestone may be formed at the bottom of the sea in about 6,000 years.

As these sedimentary rocks accumulate into new strata, their own weight forces them downward and the crust beneath them must bend downward, too. The existence of a plastic, doughlike mantle beneath the crust makes this easier to picture, particularly if the crust is regarded as "floating" on top of the mantle. Thicken it, and it will float deeper in the mantle simply because it has become heavier.

THIS may not show on the surface of the earth at all. The floor of the Gulf of Mexico, for example, is still under water, as it has been for millions of years. During that time, however, the Mississippi River has been pouring silt into the gulf until the discharge is now an estimated 30,000 feet thick at the river's delta. This enormous deposit appears to have depressed part of the floor of the gulf, forcing the existing crust many thousands of feet deeper than it once was. Judging from what has happened previously in other parts of the world, the conditions under the Gulf of Mexico today are ripe for some adjustments. In another few million years, which is only tomorrow by the reckoning of geologic time, this great mass will cause an upheaval of sufficient magnitude to thrust up large mountains in the lands surrounding the gulf—in Florida perhaps, or the West Indies. Fossils of gulf marine life may be found by some future Buffon 20,000 or more feet above sea level. There is no certainty as to when, where or how this rising will take place. We must go back once more to the hot interior of the earth for clues, and the first may be found in an attempt to answer the question, Why *is* it hot?

Scientists cannot agree on this, principally because they cannot agree on how the earth was formed. For many years the prevailing theory was that the earth was the result of a great glob of molten material thrown out by the sun, or the by-product of some cosmic celestial explosion. These ideas could account very conveniently for the molten character of the center of the earth and the cold, rocky character of its surface by explaining that the planet is now in the process of cooling off. When something cools it shrinks,

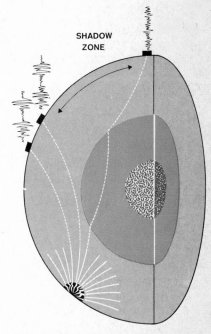

LAYERED STRUCTURE of the earth is revealed by the study of the behavior of earthquakes. In this drawing of a quarter section of the globe, a quake (bottom) sends out shock waves in all directions. These curve back to the surface (dotted lines), where seismometers time their arrival and record their intensity as wiggles on a piece of paper. The right-hand wave has fainter wiggles, and has come to the surface in the "wrong" place, indicating that it was refracted and diminished by passing through a different material in the center of the earth. This leaves a "shadow" zone where only the faintest tremors are felt. Speculation about this helped refine the present theory of earth layering.

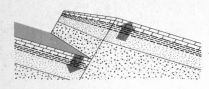

FAULTS are clean breaks in a solid land mass caused by underground pressure. Vertical breaks, occurring when one mass sinks or another is thrust up, produce sheer cliffs such as those of the Sierra Nevada in the southwestern U.S. and Mexico.

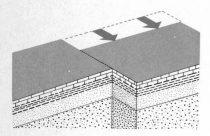

A HORIZONTAL FAULT, made by lateral pressures, may stretch for thousands of miles. A slight movement along the San Andreas fault, which runs from Mexico through California and into the Pacific, caused San Francisco's 1906 earthquake.

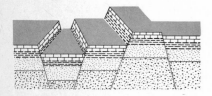

"GRABEN" AND "HORST" are technical terms for long troughs and flat-topped ridges that often occur along parallel fault lines. In the Southwest, Death Valley is an example of a graben, and many ranges in Nevada and Utah are actually horsts.

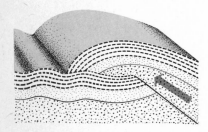

A FOLD is a buckling of earth (small ripples at left) caused when two areas of crust are pushed together. Occasionally, when pressures meet a slanting fault, as at right, a larger fold piles up, completely overriding and burying the smaller ones.

and when it shrinks its skin wrinkles—as in the classic illustration of a drying apple, which has been used over and over again to explain the presence of mountains on earth.

Unfortunately for this theory, some of the latest and most sophisticated ideas on the creation of the earth hold that it was cold at its formation, which is believed to have taken place through the coalescing of vast clouds of interstellar dust. Given a mass of such particles, mutual attraction through gravity will pull them together. As lumps grow in size, their attraction becomes stronger, and the process continues until all the matter in the celestial neighborhood has been pulled into one ball. In the case of the earth, this is still going on, as meteorites—most of which are dust particles—continue to hit the earth at a rate of 730,000 tons a year, which, distributed over the earth's surface, adds to its growth very, very slowly. The dust-cloud theory holds that the earth may not be cooling; on the contrary, it may be getting hotter, and may even be expanding. The high temperatures at the center of the earth are attributed to the influence of radioactive materials in rocks, and to pressure. The gravitational pull of the earth is very large, and the elements at the center are squeezed together by the force of the immense weight of all the material above pressing down on them. On the surface of the earth, the so-called atmospheric pressure—the weight of a column of air extending up for hundreds of miles into the sky to a point where there is no more air—is 15 pounds per square inch of earth surface. Go five miles down into the sea, and the pressure of the water is about 12,000 pounds per square inch. At the bottom of the mantle, 1,800 miles deep in the earth, the pressure is 16,950,000 pounds to the square inch, enough to set rocks flowing and reduce iron to a liquid, for under pressures like that the temperature rises to an estimated 7,000 degrees Fahrenheit deep in the mantle.

WITH such immense forces locked under our feet, it is not surprising that there will be elemental stirrings, the welling-up here and there of hotter materials, the subsiding of cooler ones, the creation of gas pockets. There is also the fact that the earth is spinning around on its own axis at a rate of 1,050 miles an hour at the equator, and that its thin crust, solid and rocklike as it may seem to us, simply is not solid enough to withstand all that activity. It even moves with the tides, the "immovable" continents actually rising and falling about six inches every day under the influence of the moon.

Still another force is believed to contribute to the instability of the earth. Under conditions as we know them on the earth's surface, all things tend to expand as they get hotter—all things, that is, except water. The cold form of water—ice—actually shrinks by about 9 per cent when it melts. Do certain rocks and other subsurface materials shrink when they melt? It is now believed that they may, through the altering of their molecular structure under the effect of intolerable heat and pressure.

To summarize, the earth may be cooling off, or it may be getting hotter. It may be contracting as it cools, or it may be expanding. It may be doing both at the same time at various points on its surface as a result of local influences. However, it is in constant motion, under constant stress, and it is these stresses that have been building mountains since there was a granite crust for mountains to be built of.

Mountains can grow in any of four ways. There can be a pushing-together of part of the earth's surface. If this is done with a rug, ripples rise up in the center. The same thing happens to the crust, and what are known as "folded" mountains result. The Appalachians, the Atlas Mountains, the Urals and the Swiss Alps all arose in this way. Although the rock may be flexible enough to bend with earth movements and show no conspicuous cracks, the violence of these changes should not be under-estimated. Accompanying the birth of the Appalachians, an ancient trough, originally 500 miles wide, was compressed to a width of 270 miles by the vigorous folding of the land.

A DIFFERENT pattern of mountain formation is distinguished by great sheer faces of rock. These are "faulted" mountains, formed when underground pressure forces one whole mass to break cleanly from another. On one side the rocks rise; on the other they subside. The separation occurs where there is a line of weakness, a fault, in the earth's crust.

Along these faults, the adjacent land masses may also shift laterally. San Francisco was almost destroyed in 1906 by a comparatively minor shift of this kind along a fault extending under the city and southward through California into Mexico and northwestward into the Pacific Ocean. The quick series of earthquakes dislocated the strata by as much as 21 feet. Later adjustments along this fault have been less violent, although in many places they have produced devastating landslides.

A succession of movements at a fault can expose a smooth mountain face on which not even a chamois or a mountain goat can find a foothold. Some of the world's most spectacular scenery consists of craggy rock walls which are the sides of great tilted fault blocks thrust toward the sky. The magnificent Sierra Nevada of California and the jagged Tetons facing the valley of Jackson Hole in Wyoming had this origin, although they, like every other mountain range in the world, are the product of more than one kind of mountain-building.

The Sierra Nevada is, in fact, the upper edge of a tremendous platform, 400 miles long and varying from 40 to 80 miles in width, that slopes into the Pacific Ocean like a huge box sunk halfway into the sea. The western edge of this mass lies nearly five miles below the ocean surface, the eastern edge rises more than two miles above sea level. Not particularly impressive when ascended from the west, since its rise is a gentle one, only about 200 feet in each mile of travel, the Sierra Nevada fairly takes one's breath away when viewed from the east. From that direction the sheer precipices of the fault are exposed.

A third way in which mountains are formed is by volcanic action, by an uprush of material from deep in the earth in sufficient quantity to actually create a mountain by depositing a huge pile of lava or cinders on the earth's surface. A recent and spectacular event of this sort occurred on February 20, 1943, when a Mexican cornfield suddenly began to produce a dense cloud of smoke. By the second day a cinder cone had reached an altitude of 100 feet. Showers of rock and fragments of gas-filled lava burst from the new volcano's throat with each rumbling explosion. They raised the peak to 450 feet in two weeks, to 930 feet in eight months and to 1,020 feet in two years. By 1952, when it stopped erupting, it was 1,350 feet high and the nearby villages of Paricutín and Parangaricutiro had been smothered under debris from the new mountain. Lava flows spread as much as six miles from the crater. Accumulations of dust and rock from the repeated eruptions destroyed every shred of vegetation for miles around.

Many of the world's great mountains were created in this fashion and grew to awesome size before man existed. We have no way of knowing today whether they are extinct or merely dormant. Their names alone suffice to conjure visions for us: Kilimanjaro, rising from the African plains almost on the equator to a snow-clad summit at 19,340 feet. Popocatépetl (17,887 feet) and Ixtacihuatl (17,343 feet)—the twin sleeping giants of Mexico—whose names roll from an Anglo-Saxon tongue only with practice. Or Fujiyama (12,389 feet)—the sacred mountain of Japan—spearing skyward from the island of Honshu. Volcanoes of lesser size have scarred human history with their eruptions: Vesuvius and Etna in Italy, Krakatoa in Indonesia, Timboro east of Java and Pelée on the West Indian island of Martinique.

THE fourth and last major process of mountain-building produces what are known as "dome" mountains. Dome mountains are produced by volcanism, but they do not act or look like typical volcanoes at all. They result from an uprush of molten rock through a crack deep in the earth, but the crack does not extend to the surface and the molten rock begins to collect in a huge pocket, much as water does in a human blister between two layers of skin. In the case of dome mountains, the skin layers are layers of crustal rock and the molten rock, welling up from below and finding no outlet, simply pushes the ground up in a round or oval-shaped bulge without rupturing it. Eventually it hardens, and if sufficient erosion occurs above it, a great dome will be revealed. The best examples of these domes in the United States are to be found in the Henry Mountains of southern Utah. The domes themselves are known as laccoliths, and when looked at from the side, are found to be shaped something like shallow gumdrops, with rounded tops and flat bottoms.

These several kinds of mountains—volcanic cones and domes, faulted and folded peaks—often rise side by side as though challenging man to sort them out. Further, they decay and erode in different ways, so that the face of the earth is marked with endlessly varying shapes.

Even as the rocks are raised into the air, the forces of erosion begin carving at the strata. Rarely does this happen at a uniform pace, as some rocks are more resistant than others. Often a river cuts down vertically, exposing level after level, like the layers in a cake. Among the most spectacular exhibits of this kind is Grand Canyon, where a vertical mile of strata has been made visible by the cleaving action of the Colorado River.

From the constant erosion that has taken place, from the folding, rupturing and refolding, it might seem impossible to reconstruct the history of any mountain. However there are clues. For nonvolcanic peaks, a most useful way of calculating their age is by studying the fossils that are found in their sedimentary rocks. These fossils are the remains of plant and animal life which became embedded in the sediments and were hardened as the sediments themselves were consolidated into rock. Since they always correspond to a definite period in the development of life on earth, and since fossils in a mountain peak could only have come from living things that grew before the mountain began to rise, a study of fossils

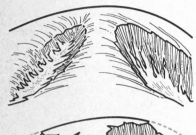

A MATTERHORN, or sharp peak, gets its shape from the erosive action of glaciers. Snow on a high, rounded summit (top) begins this process by seeping into bedrock as it melts in the sun, and wedging rock chips loose as it freezes at night. When the deepening snow hardens into glacial ice, it sweeps the fragments downhill, grinding out furrowed hollows.

The newborn glaciers widen these hollows, as indicated in the center drawing, creating between them crested divisions called arêtes. The ice, moving downhill on all sides, keeps undercutting the flanks, leaving a sharp, jagged peak in place of the original dome, shown by a dotted line.

can give an approximate date for the formation of the mountain itself.

The fossil record, therefore, is a vast calendar of the past, with an exciting progression from utterly vanished forms of life to those plants and animals alive on earth today. The most significant point in this calendar is 600 million years ago, when jellyfish, soft-bodied worms and other animals of the sea were preserved distinctly for the first time. This is the beginning of the Paleozoic era, the time of "ancient animals," which continued until about 230 million years ago. Then came the Mesozoic era, when the "intermediate animals," including the great dinosaurs, held sway, which lasted until about 63 million years ago. The last era is the Cenozoic, when the "recent animals"—the warm-blooded birds and mammals—began contesting seriously with the reptiles for a dominant place on land. Man appears among the fossils only in sediments accumulated during the last two million years.

Of the several known periods of mountain-building, at least three were completed before the beginning of the Paleozoic era, and there are almost no fossils in them to help scientists untangle their story, which is further complicated by the remains of shadowy upheavals which took place even earlier in earth history. Despite this, geologists have some idea of when they occurred, and from this can even gain a rough picture of where the continents were and what they were shaped like, although in this latter field of speculation there tend to be as many ideas about continents as there are scientists.

Thanks to fossils, however, the later periods of mountain-building present a much clearer picture. The Caledonian occurred about 400 million years ago and was responsible for a few features that still persist on the face of the globe. These are the Highlands of Scotland, the glacier-covered mass of Greenland and the Scandinavian mountains—all that remain of this ancient upheaval, although it is known that a great ridge rose all the way up the east coast of North America to Greenland, and down the west side of northern Europe through Finland, the Scandinavian Peninsula and the British Isles. It walled off the North Atlantic Ocean from the Arctic, and its peaks were among the tallest in the world at that time.

ONE hundred and seventy million years later, at the end of the Paleozoic era, another major upheaval took place. It raised new mountain chains, notably those in the eastern United States: the Adirondacks, Green Mountains, Catskills, Great Smokies and others. The present great age of these mountains is attested to by their long, low, rounded shapes. The group, generally known as the Appalachians, still has sedimentary strata, totaling nearly six miles in thickness and rich in fossils. At the same time were also produced the Urals and some east-west mountain chains just north of the present Himalayas.

A relatively quiet period followed, which marked the heyday of the dinosaurs (the Mesozoic era). For most of this time, broad marshy valleys and new shallow seas provided settling grounds for sediments and new preservation of fossils. As the mountain ranges eroded and the rivers flowed ever more languidly, there may have been little indication that stresses were intensifying within the earth's crust. Yet the world was readying itself, hoarding energy that would be spent in giving the planet many of its present lofty peaks. The fossil record shows that a few birds were flying and early mammals had already appeared among the dinosaurs when the great upheaval finally began about 70 million years ago. It affected the New World almost from Pole to Pole, raising the Andes and the Rocky Mountains. It also began the spectacular rise of the Himalayas northeast of India. Even this great spasm of rock movement did not fully expend the hoarded energy. About 15 million years ago, the planet's surface was once again deformed: the Cascade Range in America and the Alps in Europe towered toward the skies, while the Himalayas were pushed to their present eminence as the highest in the world.

Although the building-up and tearing-down of mountains results in a great deal of geologic confusion, it nevertheless brings to light things which, if the earth's crust were static, would never be seen. It has helped with the recent discovery that the crust of the continents is made of different stuff from that under the oceans. Continents are made of granite, the ocean bottom is made of a heavier kind of rock called basalt.

The light granitic continents seem to float in the heavier basalt the way an iceberg floats in water. Just as an iceberg is largely hidden, with only a small fraction of its great bulk exposed to air, so too the continents may press deeply into the basalt. They might sink in somewhat more if it were not for a counterbalancing weight supported by the basalt elsewhere: the water over the ocean bottoms. Furthermore, just as an iceberg rises from the sea as its top melts in the hot sunlight, so a mountain surges up more as it erodes away. This accounts for some of the later growth of mountains long after they appear to have reached full size. It gives meaning, too, to the idea that each major mountainous area or mountain range is actually double. One part, the smaller, is visible: the upward-pointing peaks. Below there is a larger, more rounded mass projecting downward into the earth's mantle. This theory of upside-down mountains has a name: isostasy, or balance. It explains why the crust is thicker under continents than under the sea—it would have to be to hold the continents up.

To test some of these ideas, to find out just what the state of things is at the bottom of the crust, scientists experimented for some years with a scheme to bore a hole right through to the mantle. The easiest place to do this would seem to be some point on land. But—remembering the theory of isostasy and the analogy of the iceberg—it is clear that the crust may be 30 or 40 miles deep there. To drill that distance through solid granite presents engineering problems of such hopeless complexity that the daring proposal was made to do it at sea—in deep water where the basalt layer at the bottom was suspected to be thin, perhaps only four or five miles thick. This enterprise was christened Mohole, again in honor of the Yugoslavian seismologist, A. Mohorovičić, who discovered the realm at which crust and mantle meet. In 1961 the technique of deep-sea boring was satisfactorily tested, but the project was beset by technical and financial problems and shelved. If it is resumed, samples of the mantle may actually be recovered. From them, the molecular structure of mantle material may reveal whether it does, in fact, shrink or expand under certain conditions—like ice and water. This in turn may lead to some better conclusions as to the movements deep beneath our feet. We know they take place; the lofty peaks rearing to the sky on every continent are the living evidence. But just how they work is still a mystery.

A HOGBACK RIDGE, THE EDGE OF ROCK LAYERS UPTURNED BY A MAJOR UPLIFT, CIRCLES AN ERODED PLATEAU IN NEW MEXICO

The Forces of Uplift

Over most of the land, the basic structure of the earth's crust is concealed by soil and vegetation. But by studying the naked rock of mountains, geologists have learned much about the vast forces that uplifted them, and thus about the history of the earth itself. Examples of these mountain-building forces—folding, faulting and volcanism—are shown on the following pages.

A "YOUNG" RANGE has steep, jagged contours like those of Lone Pine Peak (*left*) and 14,495-foot Mount Whitney (*right*). Part of the Sierra Nevada, they rise in a long wall of cliffs facing California's eastern border. Standing where earlier ranges were raised up and worn down, the present Sierras may be only a million years old. In this period, a brief geologic span but a time of great crustal unrest in the western United States, tremendous paroxysms of faulting ran down the Sierras' 400-mile length, raising the range 6,000 feet in places and leaving it tilted in a downward slope to the west. New uplifts accompanied a major earthquake in 1872, and some sections of the Sierras are still on the rise.

AN "OLD" RANGE in appearance as well as actual age, Vermont's Green Mountains show their maturity in a low, undulating terrain—rounded hills, gentle wooded slopes and verdant valleys crossed by slow, serpentine streams. The complex upheavals that raised the range began some 230 million years ago and continued sporadically for 160 million years. Then the Green Mountains entered a long period of relative stability. Slowly water, wind and glaciers wore down the range's highest peaks to small monadnocks and built up the valley floors with thick deposits of rocky rubble and topsoil. The leveling process may continue for millions of years before new uplifts rejuvenate the region.

High Areas of the Earth

If the oceans rose 3,000 feet, three fourths of the present land area would be under water. With the exception of inhospitable Antarctica, averaging 6,000 feet of lonely, icebound altitude, the remaining fourth is shown here: the principal mountain ranges and high plateaus of the world.

EUROPE
1 Alps
2 Apennines
3 Pyrenees
4 Scandinavian Highlands
5 Balkan Ranges
6 Carpathians

AFRICA
7 Southern African Plateaus
8 East African Highland
9 Ruwenzori
10 Ethiopian Plateau
11 Madagascar Highlands
12 Ahaggar
13 Tibesti
14 Atlas

ASIA
15 Arabian Plateau
16 Anatolian Plateau
17 Caucasus
18 Urals
19 Plateau of Iran
20 Zagros
21 Elburz
22 Karakoram
23 Kunlun
24 Hindu Kush
25 Himalayas
26 Plateau of Tibet
27 Tien Shan
28 Altai
29 Mongolian Plateau
30 Kolyma Range
31 Barisan Mountains

NORTH AMERICA
32 Rockies
33 Sierra Nevada
34 Cascades
35 Appalachians
36 Brooks Range
37 Alaskan Range
38 Mexican Plateau and mountains
39 Greenland Icecap

SOUTH AMERICA
40 Andes
41 Guiana Massif
42 Brazilian Highlands

Faulting, Folding and Volcanism

The imaginary terrain at right and the corresponding cross section of the earth's crust below it show the main types of mountains. At the left are two parallel ranges of fault-block mountains, their faces revealing layers of sedimentary rock and a black volcanic layer that were broken by the massive uplift. In the folded mountains (*left center*) the underlying strata were not fractured but corrugated by compression, forming ridges (anticlines) and valleys (synclines). Erosion has worn away the tops of the anticlines, exposing two long hard cores with elliptical hogbacks surrounding them.

At lower right are the remains of an ancient volcano—several volcanic necks or plugs which arose as molten lava, solidified in the vents of a cinder cone, and remained behind after the cone itself had been eroded away. Running off to the right from the central neck is a volcanic dike —a wall of lava that intruded into an underlying fracture and was exposed as erosion removed the softer surrounding rock. The dome mountain (*center rear*), a great up-welling of molten granite that forced itself between horizontal strata, was also exposed by erosion. Ringing the dome are two concentric hogback ridges, all that is left of the sedimentary layers that covered the dome in former times.

The forces of faulting, folding and volcanism have combined to build up the complex mountain range in the background. A composite volcano (*top right*), formed of alternating layers of cinder and lava, spews gas and ash over the alpine uplands. Snow fields, compacted into ice by melting, refreezing and their own weight, are the source of small glaciers (*top left*) which join to form a single larger glacier. As the glaciers inch downslope, they build up stripelike moraines of rock and gravel along their edges; and when they merge, their lateral moraines form a medial moraine in the center of the main glacier.

46

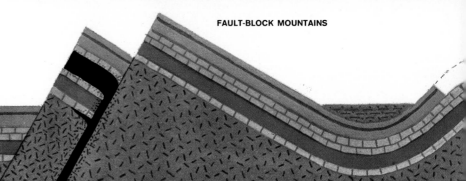

FAULT-BLOCK MOUNTAINS

FOLDED MOUNTAINS   DOME MOUNTAIN   VOLCANO

Ken Fagg

A FOLDED MOUNTAIN in Canada's Rockies clearly reveals the process that raised it. Its rock layers were bent and bulged upward by viselike pressure from opposite sides.

Mountain Sculpturing

Each of the three peaks shown at left and opposite has been raised by the mountain-building forces of folding, faulting and volcanism. Most ranges are complex—the product of more than one of these forces. And in the character of every range can be seen the work of still another force, erosion, which shapes mountains simply by wearing them down. No range is so "young" that it has not been extensively modified by erosion; and few ranges have escaped the insidious action of frost, continued and enlarged by the glaciers' massive march. Built by accumulated snows, glaciers have completely remodeled the southwest coast of New Zealand's South Island (*below*), gouging deep fiords out of a massive plateau.

GLACIATION IN A NEW ZEALAND FIORD SHAPED 5,560-FOOT MITRE PEAK (CENTER) BY CARVING OUT DEEP VALLEYS ON ITS FLANKS.

A COMPLEX MOUNTAIN near Banff in Canada is topped by layers of sedimentary rock that were broken and tilted as the folding rock mass fractured under tremendous pressure.

A DOME MOUNTAIN, Yosemite's Half Dome owes its vertical face to skinlike sheets of granite. These were cracked off by temperature changes and carried away by a glacier.

THE FIORD WAS INVADED BY THE SEA 11,000 YEARS AGO, WHEN WORLD-WIDE GLACIAL MELTING RAISED THE OCEANS 250 FEET

A VOLCANO REBORN, Wizard Island in Crater Lake rears its symmetrical cinder cone out of the submerged wreckage of a far greater volcano. Some 6,500 years ago, a mountain well over two miles high collapsed into the vast empty chamber from which its lava had flowed, leaving behind a bowl-like *caldera* six miles wide and 4,000 feet deep. Crater Lake, which half-fills the *caldera*, is the deepest lake in the United States.

51

3

Volcanoes

VOLCANOES are the mavericks of the mountains. Violent and beautiful, mysterious and changeable, they obey few of the rules that govern the behavior of ordinary mountains. The latter grow and shrink imperceptibly, but volcanoes flaunt a boom-and-bust temperament, being born in sudden, fiery cataclysms and sometimes rising over a thousand feet in a year. No two of them are alike. Not one of them maintains an identical form from one year to the next. And all of them share the unique quality, until eventual extinction, of being able to rebuild and transform themselves with molten raw material brought up from the restless viscera of the earth. Much has been learned about them, particularly in the past half century, but there is still a great deal about their causes and conduct that is an utter mystery.

From the earliest civilized times people have lived in the treacherous laps of volcanic peaks. One reason is that many volcanoes rear up on islands where land is at a premium. Another is that some of the outpourings of volcanoes make an excellent soil for crops. But the fire mountains have exacted a fearful toll among the persistent people who have crowded around their bases: in the past 2,000 years a million or more lives may have been snuffed out by volcanic activity. It is easy to comprehend the world-wide belief among ancient peoples that the dangerous peaks looming above them had supernatural qualities. To propitiate the angry mountain spirit of El Misti, the Peruvian Incas built a temple right in its crater, and often used human sacrifices to appease elemental forces which they did not understand. Even the Greeks, rational as they were, never came up with a sensible explanation of volcanoes. Aristotle shrewdly guessed that earthquakes and volcanoes were in some way associated, but he attributed the cause of both to wild underground storms. He believed that violent winds blow deep in the interior of the earth, where they burst into flames and blast into the upper air through volcanic vents. His contemporaries generally accepted the theory.

But a period of more scientific evaluation of volcanoes was beginning, and they became the subject of considerable study in the early centuries of the Christian Era. One Roman observer, Pliny the Elder, lost his life in this study, approaching Vesuvius too closely during its eruption on August 24 in A.D. 79. In a remarkable account, the first detailed record of an eruption, his nephew tells of the incident and of Pliny's intrepidity. "You might hear the shrieks of women, the screams of children and the shouts of men . . . some lifted up their hands to the gods; others were convinced that there were no gods at all and that the final endless night of which we have heard had come upon the world." But Pliny "steered directly for the dangerous spot whence the others were flying, watching it so fearlessly as to be able to dictate a description and take notes of all the movements and appearances of this catastrophe as he observed them." Finally, tarrying too long, Pliny was "choked by the thick vapors" and collapsed, one of 16,000 believed to have been killed in Pompeii alone. Many others still lie buried and unaccounted for in neighboring towns.

In the 17th Century the French philosopher Descartes decided that volcanic action was the result of huge underground conflagrations of oil, a better guess than Aristotle's but still wide of the mark. But it was not until the 20th Century that radical new tools and techniques enabled scientists to fathom the true nature of volcanic phenomena. Probing the depths beneath volcanoes with seismographs, measuring the infinitesimal changes in the topography above them with tiltmeters, subjecting volcanic ejecta to chemical analysis and making round-the-clock observations of active craters from permanent outposts perched on their rims, today's volcanologists have been slowly discovering what makes these mystifying mountains tick —and what makes them go off.

THOUGH no two volcanoes are identical twins, differences in their behavior make it possible to divide them into two fairly clear-cut types: "explosive" and "quiet." There is a wide variety of behavior in each type, but the former tends to produce the classic volcanic cone, created by the piling up of solid material through a central vent in the top. Such mountains are literally built from the ground up by their own spewings of steam and other gases, ash, rock of various kinds and lava. They may build up quickly through a series of closely spaced eruptions and then become dormant, or their growth may be slow and sporadic, spread over thousands of years. At our present level of knowledge it is impossible to determine

A "QUIET" ERUPTION occurs when lava streams from an outlet in a volcano's side after subterranean pressures have forced it up high enough in the core. This is the least violent of the three common forms of volcanic activity pictured on this page.

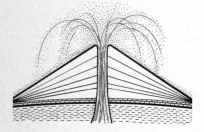

A HOT ASH ERUPTION forms a classic cone. Fiery dust, violently expelled by expanding gas, rains on the volcano's sides and builds up the symmetrical shape associated with this type. Many volcanoes alternate cinder activity with lava flows.

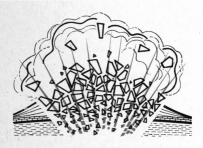

A VIOLENT ERUPTION blows out a cone composed of lava and cinders and may fling many cubic miles of rock thousands of feet. Often a new cone begins to form in the resulting crater. Vesuvius blew up once this way, as may any active volcano.

whether any recently active cone is truly "dead." All that can be safely said is that the longer it goes without erupting, the more likely it is to be dead. According to Roman tradition and history, Vesuvius had never erupted before its outburst of 79 A.D., although it smoked a bit from time to time and was obviously of volcanic origin, just as nearby Etna and Stromboli were. Since that time, Vesuvius has had scores of minor eruptions and 18 major ones, the latest in 1944. Still, no one can predict exactly when it will erupt again, or indeed that it ever will, though no scientist is so bold as to declare that Vesuvius is through.

The eruptions of some explosive cones are relatively mild but others live up to their names with a vengeance. They literally blow themselves apart. Such blasts exceed the vastest of nuclear explosions and are awesome almost beyond description. A prime example was the destruction of part of the island group of Krakatoa, in the East Indies' Sunda Strait, in 1883. This explosion caused an entire mountain to disappear. It cracked walls in Buitenzorg, Java, 100 miles away, it thrust out tidal waves which took 36,000 lives on neighboring shores, and its detonation was heard for 3,000 miles. The dust that was flung in the air did not settle until the next year, treating people all over the globe to magnificent sunsets. The great depression, or *caldera*, which it left in the mountain's place, four to five miles across and 915 feet at greatest depth, was long thought to have been the result of a blowing away of the mountaintop. But from more recent studies, volcanologists are convinced that the explosion—which blew 4.3 cubic miles of pumice and other hot rock out of the cone—emptied a subterranean chamber and brought about an *inward* collapse and engulfment of the mountaintop. A similar explosion in 1815 of the volcano Tambora on the island of Sumbawa, east of Java, killed an estimated 47,000 people, some by drowning, many more through starvation or disease.

How to draw the line between an explosion and a violent eruption is not always easy to determine, since there have been eruptions so sudden and dramatic—such as that of Mount Pelée in the Caribbean—that they can almost be classified as explosions. In the spring of 1902, St. Pierre, at the volcano's base, was one of the most prosperous communities in the West Indies. It was situated on the island of Martinique next to a ship-filled harbor against a green backdrop of sugar-cane plantations. Shadowing the town at a distance of five miles was the cone, which had been dormant for half a century and was affectionately known as "Papa Pelée" by the Pierrotins. Its summit was the scene of many a Sunday picnic. Then the seemingly impossible happened. One morning, where, only a few days before, sun-splashed houses had basked along the waterfront, a vast rubble smoldered. In the ruin lay the bodies of all but one of St. Pierre's 30,000 inhabitants, a prisoner in an underground dungeon.

Eyewitnesses from nearby towns later told how the catastrophe had come about. Pelée had not attacked without warning: for several weeks it had been unusually restless, belching smoke and ash and jarring the city with minor earthquakes. On one occasion, after a brief outburst, it had engulfed a sugar-refining factory on its flank, burying 150 workers in a torrent of scalding mud. Although some evacuated, St. Pierre's population was swollen by others flocking in from the hills.

Then, on the morning of May 8 at 7:52 o'clock, a huge vent opened in the mountain's south slope overlooking St. Pierre, and the air was shattered by a sound "like all the machinery in the world breaking down at once." Two fiery blasts of smoke belched out of the vent, one aiming straight up for seven miles into the sky, the other thrusting down the mountainside toward the port and the sea. Rolling and tumbling "like leaping lions," the incandescent cloud, loaded with particles of debris from the explosion, swept over the city at a speed estimated at five to six miles per minute. At nearby Fort-de-France the telegrapher in the post office had just finished taking down a routine news report about the state of the volcano from the telegrapher in the post office at St. Pierre. He started to tap out his acknowledgment—but the line was dead.

One question that modern research has partially answered is what was in the terrible cloud that snuffed out St. Pierre—and perhaps what was in a similar lethal Vesuvian cloud that killed 200 people in a single night in 1906, for the two catastrophes had things in common. The main ingredient is believed to have been superheated steam cooked to a blistering 1,500 degrees Fahrenheit. Suspended in the steam were tons of rock pulverized by the blast and heated to searing incandescence. This suspended rock was what gave the cloud the weight it needed to roll down the hill to St. Pierre. It is almost certain that gases were mixed in with the steam, probably carbon monoxide (the lethal fume given off by internal combustion engines) and even more deadly hydrogen sulphide. Considering the nature of this amalgam, and the ferocious heat of it, what is remarkable is that there was even one survivor of the holocaust.

A SECOND kind of volcano—and the better understood, since its activities are gentler and it can be more closely studied than the explosive type—is the shield volcano. This type is characterized by great emissions of lava which rise up through long fissures in the ground and gradually build up the wide, gently sloping and enormously thick shields which give it its name. A perfect example of this form is Mauna Loa, on the island of Hawaii, a gigantic pile of lava 70 miles long. It is far longer at its true base 16,000 feet deep in the ocean, and the entire mountain, from ocean floor to peak, is the highest in the world, topping Everest by nearly a thousand feet.

A census of the world's fire mountains would disclose several thousand cones, and relatively few of the shield volcanoes. Counting both, there are fewer than 500 individual volcanoes that are considered active today. Their distribution seems puzzling, for volcanoes are not scattered helter-skelter over the face of the earth but appear, strangely, in well-ordered ranks. There are none in the huge fold-mountain areas of the Himalayas and the Alps, and except for Africa's Great Rift Valley they are rare deep in the interiors of the continents. In curving arcs, they stretch along the Pacific edges of continents, along deep ocean trenches and major fractures of the earth's crust, and along the great island chains, like beads strung on gracefully draped necklaces. But the beads are wildly unmatched in size, shape and vigor.

Most active volcanoes lie within a belt called the "ring of fire," which loops around the Pacific Ocean and its shorelands. The southern anchor of this belt is Ross Island on the edge of Antarctica, where Mount Erebus stands in its cold white cloak of perpetual snow, flaunting an incongruous plume of steam. Extending up the west coast of South America along the

Andes, the belt takes in Aconcagua in Argentina, which is believed by some experts to be a long-dead volcano and if so is the loftiest volcanic peak in the world. In Peru and Ecuador the belt divides to take in a whole series of volcanoes, including 19,344-foot Cotopaxi, highest of all active cones, and storied El Misti, almost as high. Here also smolders Sangay, one of the most relentlessly active of volcanoes. On occasion Sangay catapults boulders the size of small houses into the air at 1,000-mile-per-hour speed.

In the Caribbean the belt bulges to enclose Pelée, Mount Misery on St. Kitts Island, and a few other West Indian cones, then doubles back to Central America. In Mexico it passes Paricutín, a cinder cone born in a cornfield in 1943 and now 1,350 feet high. Continuing up the Pacific coast, it takes in Lassen and Shasta, Hood, Rainier and Baker—all of them in the United States. In Alaska the line follows the great curve of the Aleutians past the crater of Katmai, gouged out in 1912 by one of history's great eruptions, which blanketed Kodiak, 100 miles away, under a 10- to 12-inch fall of ash. Across the Bering Strait and down Russia's Kamchatka peninsula, which has 127 volcanoes and is one of the earth's most active volcanic regions, the belt threads through the Kuriles into Japan, where Fujiyama reigns as the world's most beautiful cone. Next come Taal and Mayon in the largely lava-built Philippines, twin killers that have taken a steady toll of people in the past 100 years.

In the Celebes the Pacific ring of fire touches another arc that swings westward through Indonesia. The Pacific ring continues southward toward New Zealand by way of New Guinea and the Solomons; the other belt, anchored by infamous Krakatoa and Tambora in Indonesia, leads into the nonvolcanic mountains of Burma and the Himalayas, the volcanic peaks reappearing in the Caucasus and the Mediterranean, where lie still-active Stromboli, Vesuvius and Etna, and Vulcan, the sleeping giant for which all volcanoes are named. More volcanoes border the Red Sea and Africa's Great Rift Valley, a suspected major fracture in the earth's crust which contains snow-capped Kilimanjaro, 200 miles from the equator and the continent's highest eminence (19,340 feet).

A lesser string of volcanic peaks runs the length of the Atlantic from Iceland—scene of more than 150 eruptions since the last ice age—to tiny Tristan da Cunha, whose 269 inhabitants were evacuated in 1961 when their local volcano, The Peak, quiescent for at least four and a half centuries, suddenly spawned a brood of fire-belching infant cones. Also in the Atlantic range stand the volcanoes of the Azores, St. Paul's Rock, Ascension and lonely St. Helena, where Napoleon was exiled. In the north central Pacific, the Hawaiian volcanoes are a group unto themselves.

WHY the fire mountains are strung out across the world in this garland fashion, and why they exist in the first place, is still not fully understood by volcanologists. But a great deal is known by now about the stuff they are made of. It is called magma, and it is the raw material of all eruptions and all volcanoes as well. (It is worth remembering, by the way, that a volcano is the product and vehicle of eruption, but not the cause.)

Magma is an orange-red molten paste of rock, which wells up in the throat of a volcano during an eruption. It may be viscous, or thin as soup; it may be supercharged with steam and other gases, or bear little of these. Some magmas are heavy and alkaline; others are light and acid. All are

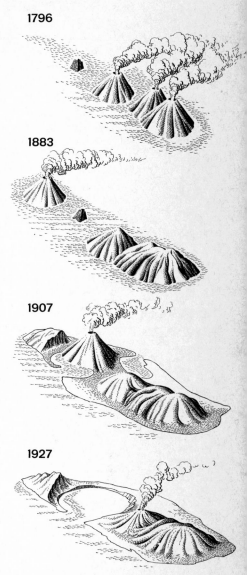

1796

1883

1907

1927

A VOLCANIC ISLAND may change its shape again and again, as these drawings of Bogoslof Island in the Aleutians demonstrate. First, in 1796, a triple volcano erupted. In 1883 another one rose a mile to the northwest of the already weathered cones of 1796. By 1907 there had been still another eruption and enough volcanic debris had fallen to form beaches. Later that year this last cone exploded with violence, leaving only a lagoon between the older peaks. In 1927 a small crater developed near the lagoon which still steams today.

extremely hot (1,800 to 2,200 degrees Fahrenheit) as they boil up from within the earth's interior.

The superheated paste surges to the surface through pipelike conduits called vents, or through long fissures that extend down through the earth's crust. Just how far down they go, and exactly what reservoirs they tap, are subjects of controversy, but most authorities believe that magma comes from the upper region of the earth's mantle. About 1,800 miles thick, this layer of hot, extremely dense rock underlies the earth's crust, which is from 22 to 37 miles thick under the continents, but as thin as two miles under the oceans. Magma may be produced by partial melting of pockets in the mantle, or it may come from a suspected shell of near-molten material in the upper mantle. No one today believes that magma comes from within the fiery core that seethes below the mantle, since present theories indicate that the core is made of a nickel-iron, and bears no resemblance at all to what comes out of volcanoes.

Bᴜᴛ why should the rock in the mantle melt at all? The key may well be the release of pressure. The weight of the earth's surface layers exerts an enormous downward push on the mantle—more than 100 tons per square inch at depths of 30 miles. By the laws of physics this should be enough to keep the rock compressed in a solid state, despite the enormous heat, which increases with depth and which might otherwise be capable of melting the rock. Therefore, if pressures deep in the earth could in some way be reduced, the rock might then melt. This presumably happens in the case of magma. We may imagine an earthquake warping a deep layer of crustal rock so that a pocket of lower pressure is created in the upper mantle under the crust. As mantle rock expands within the pocket, its density decreases and its melting temperature goes down. Soon, absorbing heat from its surroundings, it melts into magma. If the quake has also opened any fissures in the crust overlying the area, the magma will rush into them and rise toward the surface. Where it breaks through, a new volcano is created—or if the conduit is an established one leading to an already-existing vent, an old volcano erupts anew.

By whatever process it is brought to a boil, the type of magma rising in a volcano determines the nature of the eruption, whether violent or sluggish, and the type of eruption in turn determines the nature of the volcano that is formed. Obviously the eruptions that formed Fujiyama's delicate cone were dramatically different from those forming the more gently sloping but much greater bulk of Mauna Loa in Hawaii. The decisive factors about magma are two: its viscosity and its gas content. If the molten material is thick, if it rises slowly, it will have a tendency to harden and the gases may have a difficult time escaping. Collecting in bottlenecks, the contained gases build up enough pressure to clear the vent with explosive force and shatter the hardened rock into small fragments.

The escaping vapors, which may include many gases besides those in the death-dealing Vesuvian and Pelean clouds, often billow up into cauliflower-like thunderheads 30,000 feet high. The molten rock spattered aloft cools and hardens as it passes through the air, falling back to earth in a number of different forms. Chief of these is cinder, a fine black gravel resembling small furnace clinkers. Raining down around the vent, the cinder quickly piles up to form the familiar, symmetrical cone. Such cones are often found

THE NENE GOOSE, an almost extinct Hawaiian species, lives out its life on lava flows. As the animal adapted to a landlocked existence, the webs between its toes slowly shrank. Now they are only about half as large as the webs of most geese, which spend much time swimming.

in groups, or they may be strung out in a line several miles long, marking the path of a volcanic fissure or fault in the crust of the earth. Cinder cones are often reinforced with alternating layers of lava and are then called composite cones; most of the world's great volcanoes are of this type.

The finer magma spray may also fall back to earth as a fine white ash, which can become compacted into a substance known as tuff. When mixed with steam, rain or melting snow during an eruption, ash forms a heavy mud, which upon drying becomes a kind of natural concrete. Deposits of it are mined extensively near Herculaneum, from the 20-foot layer of muddy ash Vesuvius laid down there nearly 1,900 years ago, and this is often used today as a building material.

Still another eruption product is formed from magma reaching the surface when gases in it expand into myriad bubbles, creating a foamy, or frothy, material. This foam, rapidly cooling, becomes pumice, a lightweight glassy rock manufactured only by volcanoes. Volcanic blowups also produce another freakish kind of rock, the volcanic bomb. Weighing from a few ounces to hundreds of pounds, the bomb is a blob of magma which is hurled far from a vent by an explosion. Molded and hardened by their flight through the air, bombs often acquire a curious bread-roll look, smooth and ovaloid.

As far as explosions go, the one at Krakatoa was the mightiest of modern times. In America, Crater Lake is an example of what such a blast can do. The ancient volcano that commanded the site is now known as Mount Mazama. When it blew up, 6,500 years ago, approximately 17 cubic miles of rock were displaced. Since only 7.5 cubic miles of ejecta have been found near the lake, the conclusion is that most of Mount Mazama was swallowed up in its own crater.

Few volcanic eruptions are that violent. When the consistency of the emerging magma is thin and its gas content is low, a comparatively peaceful boiling-over occurs. The greater part of the magma escapes over the crater's rim or through rifts in the mountain's flanks in a fiery flow of lava which may engulf whole towns but rarely kills anyone. Such flows average 10 feet in thickness and may move as fast as 35 miles an hour. If the flow cools quickly, it may harden into shiny black glass. If it cools more slowly so that the basalt has time to crystallize, it turns into the material for which volcanoes are best known, black lava rock. Lava itself comes in several forms. Smooth and ropy-surfaced lava, called "pahoehoe" in Hawaiian, is so folded and creased that it looks like poured molasses. Rough lava, called "aa," is crumbled and coarse, and the rare pillow lava has the look of a carelessly tossed pile of sandbags.

Sometimes magma escapes from underground so quietly that no volcanic mountain is formed. Some 30 million years ago successive thin flows poured from a number of long fissures in the American Northwest, to create a huge tableland of solid lava. Now overspread with sagebrush, forests and farms, the Columbia lava field is not easily recognized, but it covers 200,000 square miles of Washington, Oregon and Idaho with hundreds of basalt layers that exceed several miles in total thickness.

Long after they become extinct, some volcanoes are eroded to a hardly identifiable shape: all that is left is an odd skeleton of lava that traces the path taken by magma to get to the surface during the volcano's youth.

The backbone of such a skeleton is a steep tower, or plug, of black rock that stands where the cone once grew. This is the central neck, the magma-filled throat of the mountain, which hardened into dense rock and, being tougher than the cinder cone and located inside it, resisted erosion much longer. Radiating out from the plug are usually a number of tapering, sharp-ridged walls or dikes of solidified rock. These were rifts in the mountain's flanks up which the magma also flowed, and they too have resisted erosion. The world's leading example of this phenomenon of volcanic senility is Shiprock, in New Mexico.

From newborn Paricutín to mummified Shiprock, scientists have examined volcanoes in every stage of life and death. The study is intimately linked to the larger study of the familiar yet mystical earth beneath our feet. If we knew more about the earth and its origins and its impenetrable insides, we should learn more about volcanoes; and every added fact that is nailed down about volcanoes leaves the earth that much less inscrutable. Geologists have discovered, for example, that the belts of volcanoes are also centers for other kinds of crustal disturbances. All the world's deep earthquakes and many of its shallow ones originate under these fire-mountain chains. All the youngest folded-mountain ranges, like the cordilleras on the California coast, follow the same directional lines. Parallel to them are the six-to-seven-mile-deep trenches in the ocean floor that have baffled science ever since their discovery early this century. Everything indicates that the active volcano belts are zones of tremendous strain in the earth's crust, zones along which deep fissures are being formed that give rise to volcanoes and other phenomena.

One notion of how such fissures may be produced was advanced by Alfred Wegener. He believed that the massive changes occurring along the volcanic belts are largely caused by the continents slipping sideways over the mantle. According to this theory the continents are not firmly bonded to the mantle at all but are floating over it, and the easterly rotation of the earth creates a frictional tidal drag that slowly pulls the continents westward. Over millions of years this kind of drift would explain, along with the theory that the location of the poles has shifted, the fact that tropical vegetation once thrived at the present sites of the poles. In Wegener's view, it has been the westward pull on land masses that has caused the pile-up of mountain chains all along the Pacific coast of North and South America. And the inexorable wrench that piled up the mountains has also undercut them with deep cracks—the feeder lines used by volcanoes to bring magma to the surface.

Two other theories that try to account for volcano fissures take diametrically opposite views of what is happening to the earth. As noted in Chapter 2, one school holds that the globe is slowly shrinking; the other argues that it is gradually expanding; and there is evidence on both sides. The concept of contraction is an old one, based on the idea that the earth is cooling down from an original incandescent state and is therefore getting smaller, wrinkling and crackling like an apple in the process.

The newer theory of an expanding world has as its basis the idea that the globe began as a cool cloud of interstellar gas. As this cloud condensed into a cold planet it slowly grew hotter from radioactive heating, and the heating process is still going on. Most substances expand when heated and in the view of Columbia University's Bruce Heezen the earth is doing likewise. What proves this, he holds, is the existence of the Mid-Ocean Ridge. This underwater mountain chain that runs through most of the oceans of the world is split along much of its length by an odd, V-shaped rift many thousands of feet deep and several miles wide. Many undersea earthquakes originate in the vicinity of this ridge, most of them just below the center of the rift. Heezen believes the rift, particularly the section that lies in the Atlantic Ocean, is a major crustal fracture pried open by expansion, and that the earthquakes show that expansion is still going on, one of its results being the crustal cracking that releases the raw material for volcanoes.

According to a fourth theory, of F. A. Vening Meinesz, slow currents are astir in the stiff yet plastic rock of the earth's mantle; these slow stirrings—caused by temperature differences in the crust—lead to the forces which buckle and tear the more rigid crustal layers. Still another school declares that there is no such thing as a plastic mantle; the earth is a rigid solid and volcanoes are merely tapping layers of rock that have been accidentally melted into magma by tremendous concentrations of subterranean heat.

Obviously the evidence is not all in, so theories will keep right on erupting. A fascinating new one, advanced by J. Tuzo Wilson, would have it that volcanoes are actually responsible for the formation of continents. From studies of volcanic archipelagoes like the Aleutians and the Kuriles, he concluded that new volcanic island chains rising out of the sea through millions of years tend to form alongside older similar chains. Then, after more millions of years, sediment washed down from the peaks by erosion gradually fills in the narrow water-spaces between the islands. As the mountain-building processes continue, deeper and deeper layers of sediment are formed, and eventually are compacted into rock themselves and become part of the continent's granitic crust. Indeed, the shifting of this vast weight of material from mountain peak to basin may supply the force for further mountain-building. It is possible that in time a series of parallel chains forms, fanning slowly outward like ripples in a pond and eventually leading to the build-up of an entire continental mass.

Most of this chapter has dealt with the violent aspects of volcanism which are hostile to man. The story has another side, the beneficence of the volcanoes, to which man may even owe his existence. It is quite probable that volcanoes are responsible for the air we breathe and the water we drink. For, along with the noxious gases they exhale during eruptions, they send out the basic ingredients of the earth's atmosphere. Among these are nitrogen, hydrogen and carbon dioxide. The last serves to support plant life, which in turn releases oxygen into the atmosphere by the process of photosynthesis. These gases are also given off by small volcanic vents called fumaroles, thousands of which are found in Yellowstone Park. Volcanoes, moreover, are also sources of water, producing it by combining hydrogen and oxygen in their furnaces and ejecting it as blasts of steam. Much of this water, however, is actually ground water seeping slowly downward into reservoirs of hot magma deep underground. Free-flowing volcanic sideshows like mudpots, geysers and hot springs are almost entirely supplied by this second source. How important volcanoes and fumaroles are to man's well-being may be seen from the fact that the production of gases over a period of several billion years by

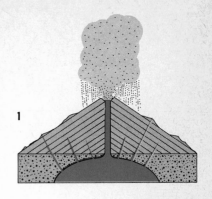

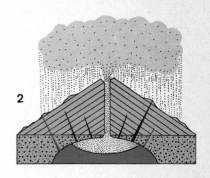

A VOLCANO'S COLLAPSE can produce a "caldera," or volcanic pit, as shown in these drawings of the destruction of Oregon's Mount Mazama 6,500 years ago. The peak began to spew a froth of gas and pumice (1). When much of this material had been blown from the mountain, there remained an immense underground cavity (2), into which the 12,000-foot peak fell (3) when internal pressures subsided.

these two sources could have created all of the earth's present atmosphere.

There are a number of localized benefits conferred by these fire-breathing mountains: therapeutic hot springs in many countries, free steam heat for schools in Iceland and Japan, abundant hot water for laundries in New Zealand, electric power in Italy. But the most widespread benefit is the fertility which many volcanoes impart to the soil all around them. Volcanic ejecta may not enrich soils directly, the way fertilizer does; there is a dispute about the amount of nutrients such as potash and phosphates which it contains. One secret of its efficacy may be the porous water-holding quality it gives the soil.

In such a favored yet threatened area, not even a violent eruption interferes with the lush plant life for long. After Krakatoa's explosion and collapse in 1883, all that was left was a low stump of a peak, thickly covered with hot, vile-smelling ash. Yet only three years later a Dutch botanist found grass and ferns already taking root in the thin beginnings of new soil. In 10 years the island was green again, supporting a number of coconut trees, and by 1930 it was back to its pre-catastrophic state—an impenetrable tangle of tropical forest.

SOMEDAY, it may be, volcanoes will be known primarily for the benefits they bestow, and only incidentally as menaces among mountains. This can come about through eruption prediction, a study already well developed in the present century. Rough prediction is possible because nearly all volcanoes announce their eruptions in advance. Sometimes the danger signals start years before the blast with hints that scientific instruments can detect. Among the signs may be subtle swarms of nearly imperceptible earth tremors, or a slight bulging of the cone caused by magma welling upward; some shield volcanoes like Kilauea are most accommodating in giving such early warnings of a forthcoming flow. Sharper, local, near-surface quakes often immediately precede Hawaiian eruptions. Other volcanic danger signals include increase in temperature of the water in hot springs and of the gas in fumaroles near the cone. Vibrations like subterranean thunder can sometimes be heard. The final warning is sporadic extrusion of gases and ash. The present status of the art of volcano prediction is much like that of predicting the stock market. The basic indicators of economic growth can be likened to the swelling of the volcano from increasing magma stored below. But just when the stock market, or the volcano, will go up rests on variables still not fully understood. Nevertheless, man can and has acted on the warnings that volcanoes give.

Hearing and seeing such danger signs, a Japanese community in the shadow of a volcano saved itself from destruction in 1912, in a manner that stands as an example for peoples in other volcanic areas. Sakurajima, located on an island in a busy harbor not unlike St. Pierre's had a volcano's typically fertile slopes and was home to thousands of farm families. When the warning quakes and rumblings began, the authorities acted quickly. They ordered a huge fleet of sampans into the harbor, and at least 23,000 people were evacuated. A day after they sailed away, Sakurajima exploded in one of the most massive eruptions in Japanese history. Having escaped its fury, the people returned, and today their children and grandchildren till fertile new fields that overlie the old ones. Though foiled, Sakurajima has held no grudge.

A CLOUD OF ASH AND STEAM EMERGES FROM VESUVIUS IN 1944. THIS WAS THE VOLCANO'S 18TH RECORDED MAJOR ERUPTION

Mountains of Fire

Volcanoes have always played a dual role. Erupting gases, ash and molten rock, they have caused great havoc throughout history. The names Krakatoa, Vesuvius, Pelée are synonyms for violence and death. But volcanoes are indispensable to life. To their activity we owe much of the air we breathe, the water we drink and the fertility of some of the world's best farmland.

A ROMANTIC CONCEPTION OF "THE LAST DAY OF POMPEII" WAS PAINTED BY THE RUSSIAN COURT ARTIST K. P. BRULOW ABOUT 1830

Pompeii's Violent End

The most famous eruption in history was the blast that wiped out the Roman city of Pompeii in 79 A.D. Mount Vesuvius, after centuries of quietude, suddenly awoke to bombard the luxurious coastal resort for three days with a driving rain of pumice and ash. Some of the population escaped, but it is estimated that 16,000 perished under debris that piled up to 20 feet deep. So quickly did the volcano strike that many Pompeians were buried where they stood, and molds of their bodies have been found perfectly preserved in the ash. The debacle, although fatal to one of the classical world's most beautiful cities, proved a boon to future generations by creating a unique record of Roman life and its Greek artistic inheritance.

The most minute details of Pompeian architecture were kept in excellent condition for centuries. The massive stone blocks of what were once Roman roads still show clearly the imprint of ancient chariot wheels. Eggs, about to be cooked centuries ago, survived with their shells unbroken. Vesuvius has also proved a boon to modern Italian farmers. The ash laid down by the volcano's frequent subsequent eruptions over a 1,900-year period has formed much fertile soil so that some of Italy's richest crops of grapes and oranges are grown on its slopes.

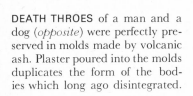

DEATH THROES of a man and a dog (*opposite*) were perfectly preserved in molds made by volcanic ash. Plaster poured into the molds duplicates the form of the bodies which long ago disintegrated.

FOCUS OF LIFE in Pompeii was the Forum (*right*), which housed the city's law court. Its tall columns, typical of the classical architecture of the city, are viewed each year by over 600,000 tourists.

How Pelée Killed St. Pierre

An eruption as sudden and destructive as the one that snuffed out Pompeii overwhelmed the port of St. Pierre on the West Indian island of Martinique in 1902. St. Pierre lay at the foot of Mount Pelée, a volcano which had shown signs of activity only twice in a hundred years. Then, unexpectedly, it began spewing ash and black smoke. Sulphur fumes became so thick that people were forced to go around with kerchiefs over their faces, and horses were suffocated in the streets. Soon earthquakes shook the island daily and ominous thunder rolled deep underground. As these danger signs increased, many people thought of evacuating, but they were reassured by the actions of the island's governor. Convinced that all was well, he made the dramatic gesture of moving his family from the capital of Fort-de-France into residence in St. Pierre.

A few days later, on the morning of May 8, a huge crack burst open in Pelée's flank. Out of it roared an incandescent cloud of steam, other gases and dust, which in less than a minute engulfed St. Pierre, reducing it to a ruin. Rescuers came immediately from Fort-de-France but, because the ground was too hot to walk on, were unable to go ashore for hours. When they did, they found only three people alive. The first, a woman in her kitchen, died within minutes of when she was found. The second, a man, had managed to run as far as the suburbs of St. Pierre, but he also died soon afterward.

Three days later, a third survivor was heard crying for help deep in the smoking rubble. The voice came from a dungeon in the city jail. There, terribly burned but still living, was a young Negro named Ludger Sylbaris. He had survived the holocaust because his cell was fitted with only a tiny grate-window which had kept out the full force of Pelée's cloud. Sylbaris said that he had heard no sound and seen no fire and that the excruciating heat had lasted only a moment. That terrible moment, however, had been sufficient to kill 30,000 people—every one of the citizens of St. Pierre except Ludger Sylbaris.

A DOME OF LAVA is thrust from Mount Pelée's crater (*opposite*) by gas pressure deep within, a phenomenon often associated with the volcano's eruptions.

ANOTHER DEATH CLOUD rises above shattered St. Pierre as Mount Pelée erupts again. After the original holocaust the town remained deserted, so this cloud, late in 1902, did no damage. Rubbled and lifeless, St. Pierre is seen below in a photograph taken shortly after the first eruption.

ANAK KRAKATOA, LITERALLY "CHILD OF KRAKATOA," IS A NEW CINDER CONE RISEN ON THE SITE OF THE GREAT ERUPTION OF 1883

Krakatoa and Its Child

Unlike that old performer, Vesuvius, the volcanic island of Krakatoa in the East Indies was comparatively unknown prior to 1883. In that year the most spectacular volcanic explosion of history shattered Krakatoa, pulverizing 4.3 cubic miles of mountain and scattering it into the atmosphere. The noise of the blast was heard 3,000 miles away, and 100-foot waves smashed against the coasts of Java and Sumatra, killing 36,000 people. In 1930 a cone (*above*) rose in the lagoon formed in 1883, presaging a new build-up of explosive forces under the sea. Geologists say that Krakatoa may blow up again.

FAR-FLUNG BOULDER of several tons is one of many cast up by Anak Krakatoa in recent eruptions. The deep pit behind the rock shows where it bounced before stopping.

THREATENING CLOUD blacks out the sky during an eruption of Anak Krakatoa (*opposite*). Observers advance cautiously to the crater rim under a dangerous rain of debris.

Hawaii's Shield Domes

The 28 South Pacific islands that make up the state of Hawaii include the world's finest examples of a unique kind of volcano: the shield dome. Totally different from cones like Fuji-yama, the Hawaiian volcano is broad and flat, its summit usually topped by a wide, shallow depression. It is the product of a relatively quiet eruption of free-flowing lava.

When Kilauea Iki (*right*) became active in 1959, there was no violent explosion, only a series of fountainlike bursts of glowing gas and lava. Two months later this was followed by an outpouring of fast-moving lava from nearby fissures which, after three weeks, had spread over almost 2,000 acres. Such fluid flows are what give shield domes their special shape. Successive flows of lava, spreading out from long cracks in the earth, gradually pile up to form the dome outline. In the vicinity of the cracks may be found small cones and craters. Large though it appears, Kilauea Iki is only one such crater on the flank of Kilauea, a gigantic shield dome that rises 20,000 feet from the bottom of the Pacific.

SILHOUETTED TOURISTS view Kilauea Iki's brilliant display. The quiet nature of most Hawaiian eruptions makes it fairly safe to observe them closely.

FIRE FOUNTAIN, bursting from Kilauea Iki (*right*), is a column of gas, 1,000 feet high, filled with fiery lava fragments. A deep molten pool glows in the crater.

THE THUNDEROUS FINALE of Kilauea Iki's 1959 eruption came with this burst, which hurled a stream of lava and chunks of rock 1,250 feet in the air. The blast occurred one week after the explosions began, and lasted for several seconds. Eight hours later, all activity ceased. This photograph, taken from a cliff that rims the crater just 200 feet away from the molten column, shows the silhouette of grass and brush in the foreground, burned out from the intense heat.

Pahoehoe and Aa

Lava is the most copious and familiar product of volcanoes. As it emerges from the volcano, molten and charged with gas—in this state it is called "magma"—it governs the kind of eruption that takes place. If the magma is thick and impregnated with gas, it erupts explosively, burst apart by the escaping gas. When thin and low in gas, it flows evenly and quietly, as lava, down the volcano's flanks. Such flows vary in nature. The lava may harden into a rough rock, called "aa," or it may congeal into smooth folds, called "pahoehoe." Its flow may vary from a few hundred feet a day up to 35 miles an hour. The source of magma remains a mystery, but it is probable that much of it comes from depths down to 40 miles in the region of the earth's mantle.

GLOWING BRIGHTLY UNDER A SMOOTH, BLACK CRUST OF HARDENING ROCK, A FAST FLOW OF PAHOEHOE LAVA FROM KILAUEA

BLOBS OF LAVA explode out of a small knoll, called a spatter cone (*opposite*). Rarely more than 10 feet high, these cones form along volcanic fissures like those found flanking Hawaii's shield domes.

BLAZING HOUSE in Kapoho, Hawaii, is crushed under a lava flow during Kilauea's 1960 eruption (*right*). Kapoho was evacuated safely, but became the first U.S. town to be wrecked by a volcano.

STREAMS DOWN A ROAD IN HAWAII. HIGH IN TEMPERATURE AND EXTREMELY FLUID, HAWAIIAN LAVAS MAY FLOW 60 MILES IN A DAY

FURROWED FLANK of an extinct shield volcano rises above a rich valley on the island of Oahu, Hawaii's political capital. The slow grinding of erosion has created a sharp-edged ridge, down whose sides run deep channels. The well-worn cliff is still able to support a considerable covering of vegetation, including kukui trees, low shrubs and evergreens.

A COLUMN OF LAVA forms a 279-foot pedestal for the chapel of St.-Michel d'Aiguilhe (*opposite*) in Le Puy in southern France. The steep-sided tower, which once served to protect the chapel, is probably the lava-filled throat of a long-dead volcano, most of which eroded millions of years ago. Remnants of ancient volcanoes abound in France.

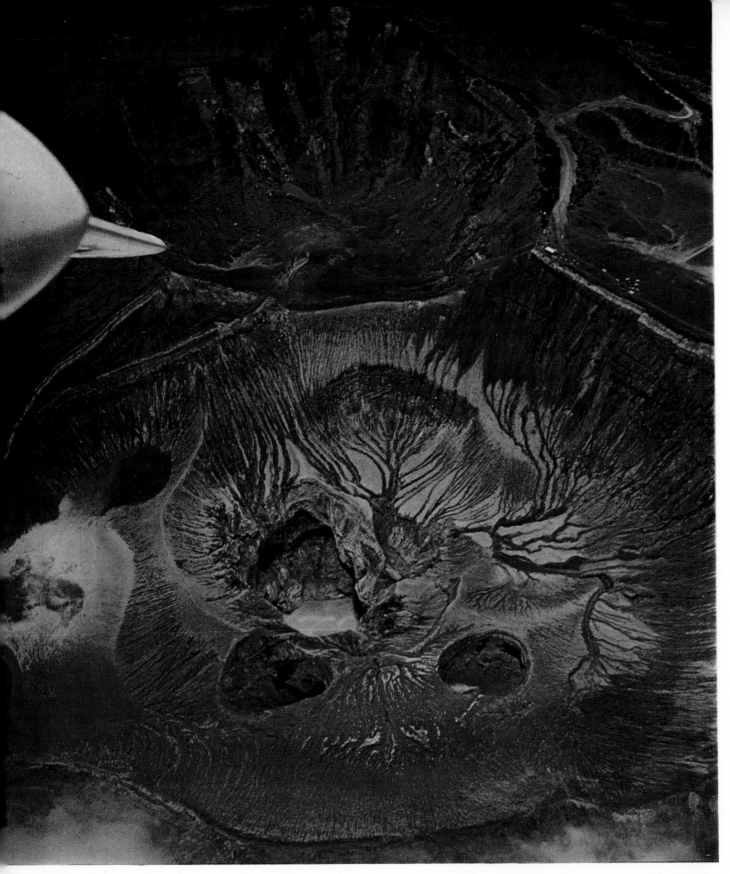

INTERIOR OF A CRATER, in Costa Rica's Irazú volcano, reveals a cavity that is over a mile wide and contains three smaller explosion craters formed at different times in the volcano's long history. Irazú erupted violently in 1723 and still sends up steam and ash. The automobiles and house visible at upper right give an idea of its great size.

CIRCULAR MUD POOLS mixed with pulverized lava seethe at the surface of a field of springs and geysers in northern New Zealand (*opposite*). Superheated vapors rise from below, creating a layer of bubbles, each of which slowly swells and bursts, adding a new ring to the porridgelike material. The individual eddies are about two yards across.

A STURDY PINE clings to a rock
high in the Swiss Alps. This slow-
growing species requires sunlight
and will not flourish in protected
hollows, where it may be covered
over by blankets of drifting snow.

4

Plants, Winds and Ice

THE previous chapters of this book have dealt with mountains principally as geologic phenomena, as things that stick up high above the
surface of the earth and whose height alone makes them mountains. To the
biologist mere height is of secondary importance. It is the *results* of that
height which fascinate him. Mountains produce the most bewildering con-
trasts in living conditions for both plants and animals that may be found
anywhere on the globe. These conditions are harsh almost beyond belief.
They impose problems of survival in the face of winds that blow with
constant ferocity, in the face of cold, of wildly fluctuating temperatures, of
floods of rain or none at all, of rocky sliding soil, of snow and ice, and of
atmosphere that contains little oxygen but a great deal of radiation. Furthermore, conditions are not necessarily the same on two mountains in the
same range, or on two mountains on opposite sides of the same valley, or
even at different levels of the same mountain.

   A mountain may be compared to an accordion in the sense that it com-
presses into a very short space conditions which on the flat would be spaced
over thousands of miles. Set a man down at random in a grassland or

prairie in mid-continental United States, start him walking north, and after a time he will notice that his surroundings have begun to change. Small clumps of broad-leaved trees will appear. As he travels, these clumps will become groves, and will finally expand into a continuous forest. Proceeding north, he will rather suddenly find himself in another kind of forest, the dense evergreen stands of pine, fir and spruce, which blanket the northern United States and southern Canada. Pushing on through Saskatchewan into the Northwest Territories, he will eventually find the trees thinning out. They will become progressively smaller and sparser until there are none, and once again he will be out in the open. But there will be no prairie grass here. Instead there will be tundra, a treeless arctic waste covered with mosses, lichens, sedges and dwarfed flowering plants. Finally, even this hardy cover will vanish, and at the end of his trip the traveler will find himself in the polar region's perpetual ice and snow.

Such a journey would take many days and would cover about four thousand miles. There is, however, a far easier way of experiencing the same vegetation changes: simply place the traveler at the base of a mountain like Pikes Peak and head him uphill. During his climb, he can study similar vegetative evidence, arranged in the same convenient strata, that a long walk toward the North Pole might reveal.

The common denominator here is, of course, cold. It gets colder as one goes north, just as it does as one goes up a mountain—but the reasons are different. Low temperatures at the poles come from the tilt of the earth's axis relative to the sun, whereas low temperatures on mountains come from dry air, which does not hold heat.

Although, as a rule of thumb, temperatures drop from three to five degrees with every thousand-foot rise in altitude, mountains display no uniformity in coldness or even in the kind of weather that may swirl about their peaks. Their location determines this. Tropical mountains are spared the cyclonic storms and attendant drastic weather changes of the temperate and polar regions, and as a result they have a climate all their own. The weather at their bases is very warm, and although they will cool off with altitude at the same rate as other mountains, one simply has to go higher before one encounters snow. The Ecuadorian city of Quito, perched at 9,350 feet in the Andes, lies almost on the equator, and has a year-round average temperature of 55 degrees—and a difference of less than a degree between its coldest and warmest months. In the American Sierras the seasonal difference at 9,350 feet may be as great as 30 degrees.

However much they differ individually, mountains retain much in common. All have climates which bear little resemblance to those of their

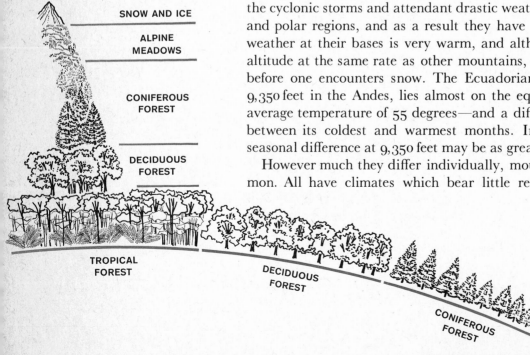

SNOW AND ICE

ALPINE MEADOWS

CONIFEROUS FOREST

DECIDUOUS FOREST

TROPICAL FOREST

DECIDUOUS FOREST

CONIFEROUS FOREST

TUNDRA MEADOWS

BANDS OF VEGETATION follow a similar sequence going up a mountain and from south to north on the flat. In this idealized view of a mountainside and a 40-degree arc of the North American continent, both begin with jungle and proceed in the same order to tundra meadow.

surrounding lowlands. And each is banded with horizontal layers of totally different kinds of trees and shrubs following each other in a fascinating sequence. The higher the zones, of course, the harsher the life. To see how this zoning system works, let us travel, from base to summit, up a typical peak in the Colorado Rockies, stopping to observe some characteristic plant populations along the way.

The first thing an observer will notice as he starts up the slope of one of the Rockies is that most broad-leaved trees tend to stick to the valleys and that a mountainside is almost exclusively the domain of fir and pine. But each zone has its own conifers. On the lower slopes of the Colorado Rockies, juniper trees and ponderosa pines abound, but the ponderosa is the hardier of the two, and a little higher up the juniper has faded out and the pine rules by itself.

The next zone reaches to about 9,500 feet in the Colorado Rockies, and is populated by dense stands of Douglas fir. Above it will be found a forest of spruce and subalpine fir. The dark, spiky-needled spruce with its hanging cones and the lighter, soft-needled fir with upright cones always go together. These two kinds of trees help each other. Spruce grows slowly but lives long; it provides a stable basis for a forest. Fir, though shorter-lived, grows rapidly and casts an abundance of seeds. This quickly produces a grove, which is important on mountains since the force of the wind is greatly reduced as it blows through a grove; individual trees are thus less likely to be blown down than single exposed specimens standing alone.

One thing which may puzzle the observer as he climbs is that the common diagrams of mountains, showing the various zones or bands of vegetation neatly divided by straight lines, are somewhat too simplified. The zones are there, all right, but irregular terrain with differences in exposure to sun and wind, in soil, and in rainfall blur the boundaries. Where conditions permit, the vegetation of one zone will invade the next higher zone, or the next lower.

AFTER climbing for hours through dense groves of fir and spruce, the hiker will begin to notice that the trees are becoming smaller and more thinly spaced. Gradually they dwindle into a stunted, wind-bent scraggle of ground-hugging vegetation called *Krummholz*, which is a German word meaning "crooked wood." This is the region where trees make their last stand against the mountain elements; it marks the timber line and the beginning of the zone of alpine tundra.

Tundra is a Russian word of Lappic origin, and in the Scandinavian countries it means the arctic regions north of where the last trees grow. When they refer to high-mountain environments these people use the word alpine; they speak of alpine meadows, alpine heaths, alpine bogs. But tundra is tundra the world over. Well-traveled scientists say that if they were to cup their eyes with their hands and look only at a narrow section of tundra, they would be hard put to tell whether they were in the Rockies, Labrador or Lapland. Much of the tundra, even in the high mountains, is gently rolling land, littered with rocks, broken by occasional peaks and cliffs. During most of the year these heights are barren. Here and there are pockets of snow lying amid wind-blown stretches of bare rock and brown patches of dead or dormant vegetation. The winds blow here throughout the year, sometimes at 100 miles an hour, and blinding snow may come whirling in at any season. Winter is eight months long, spring is scarcely more than a flicker, summer starts in June and lasts only to mid-August. It is difficult to believe that this short season will bring a blaze of flowering color, and the scurry and whir of animal life.

American scientists often call some of the tundra vegetation "belly plants" because each plant is so small that a person must lie flat on his stomach to get a good look at it. Both the colloquial and scientific names for some of the high-mountain plants suggest the nature of those that can survive on the heights. Among such names may be found the following: *prostrata* (prostrate), *procumbens* (leaning forward), *caespitosa* (clumped or tufted), *megarrhiza* (large bulb or root), *acaulis* (without stem) and *humilis* (humble).

Alpine flowers *are* small and humble, and they grow very slowly. After 10 years of continuous observation of high-mountain plants in an experimental station high in the Rockies, alpine ecologists from the University of Colorado found that a typical cushion plant seedling put out only two minute leaves a year and achieved a total growth of about a third of an inch in that entire 10-year period.

Such slow growth is enforced on mountain plants by the shortness of the summer. They must also deal with the formidable quartet of cold, wind, unstable soil, and too much or too little water. In combination these deadly hazards multiply their effectiveness. Low temperature and wind together become a "wind chill" factor, something worse than either wind or cold alone. As anyone knows who has walked abroad in a northern winter, more heat may be drained from the body by a combination of 32-degree temperature and 50-mile wind than by zero temperature and no wind. Temperature variation alone is bad enough. After staying below freezing for months on end, the soil temperature may soar to 115 degrees among the sunny rocks of a mountain slope on a midsummer day, only to fall below freezing again that night. If exposed to those extremes, a lowland plant would expire in a few hours. But mountain vegetation is equipped with a multitude of adaptations, chief among which is timing. These plants simply lie dormant during cold weather and do what growing they can during the summer. But if summers are short and growth as slow as described, a seed cannot mature and produce seeds of its own in a single season. That is why nearly all mountain plants are perennials; they live from year to year just as trees do, gradually storing up the energy to produce flowers. An annual—a plant which lasts for only one year and depends on a new crop of seeds each year to perpetuate itself, like so many of the flowers found growing in lowland gardens—will find life next to impossible on a mountaintop. In fact, of more than 300 species of flowering plants above timber line in the Rockies, only two are annuals. One of these produces blossoms only the size of a pinhead.

Even perennials have a hard time. One of the most numerous and successful is the cushion pink, or moss campion, a small cushion-shaped affair.

MIGRATING VEGETATION is a common phenomenon on high, windy slopes and is illustrated by the drawings (below) of the Rocky Mountain limber pine. A sapling takes root in the lee of a protecting rock, then begins to put out branches (2) which, bent downward by the wind, also take root. Each winter all of that year's upward growth, unprotected by the snow (3), is killed by cold, dry winds. Eventually the old parts of the tree begin to die (4) but still serve as protection, taking the place of the rock and permitting the tree to continue its migration (5).

1

2

3

A seed of one of these plants contains enough stored energy so that if it falls in a favorable spot it will be able to begin to put out roots and a stem. But mountainsides are notoriously dry throughout much of the year, and most plant energy will have to go into roots, since the larger a plant's root system, the better its chance of locating water. Large roots also help secure a plant to a slope where rocky rubble is continually sliding, and where the wind may be strong enough literally to tear away vegetation that is not securely anchored; a moss campion that is two inches high above the surface of the ground may have a root structure that goes down into the soil for two feet or more.

It may take as long as 10 years before the cushion pink is sufficiently well established to produce its first flower. When it finally comes into full bloom after about 20 years, the number of flowers it may produce is surprising. In season it may be covered with several hundred tiny pink blossoms, these set in a cushion only a foot across.

The cushion shape of the pink is itself an adaptation countering wind and cold. Just as forest trees survive chilling winds better when they grow in groves, so do the closely matted stalks of the pink. It is a miniature forest in itself, hugging the ground as an inconspicuous dome below the cold winds whistling by overhead. The importance of lowness cannot be overestimated. A man standing on an exposed mountain slope may be blown over by the wind. If he sits down he notices that its force has considerably abated. If he lies down with his face to the ground, he will be astonished to discover that the wind blowing past his cheek seems to have virtually disappeared. This is because the stable earth exerts a frictional force which resists the moving air, dragging on it and slowing it down. The effect is greatest close to the ground. Irregularities in the surface, such as outcrops of rock or small hollows, also provide protection to a remarkable extent. To a half-inch plant, a one-inch pebble may be as good a windbreak as the side of a house.

ALTHOUGH mountain air is dry and cannot retain heat at night, the sun does beat down in blistering fashion during the day, and there is nothing to prevent a plant from soaking up a good deal of this heat. The problem is to retain it. Again the cushion pink's form comes into play. Its tangle of foliage is a veritable heat trap; it absorbs and conserves sunlight much more efficiently than could any single-stalked plant. Temperature measurements taken of a cushion pink show that its interior may be as much as 20 degrees warmer than the surrounding air. Insects, which become torpid with cold, find in the depths of the cushion pink and similar plants a haven of warmth. As they crawl around in there, they may perform the function, vital to nearly all plants, of cross-pollination. So it is possible to speculate that the cushion pink's adaptations against cold may also be advantageous adaptations in the struggle to perpetuate itself, for insects are not common on the heights and tend to be blown away by the wind. Because of this scarcity, many mountain plants depend on the wind for cross-pollination.

4

5

Still others, like the *Festuca ovina*, are capable of fertilizing themselves.

One reason that mountains are windy is that the velocity of wind increases with altitude. Another is that when wind velocity doubles, its force quadruples. Further, winds pick up speed when forced through narrow places. Like a stream encountering a constricted channel, a wind confronted by two adjoining peaks may blow with extra violence through the gorge between. Not all mountains are equally windy. There are worldwide wind patterns, prominent among them the great west-to-east wind belts which rush in a continuous stream around the globe in the temperate latitudes of the Northern and Southern Hemispheres. Tropical mountains tend to be less windy than temperate ones. The highest wind velocity ever recorded was atop New Hampshire's Mount Washington, where gusts were measured at 231 miles per hour, and the average velocity over a full 24-hour period was 129 miles per hour.

With such forces ripping at the peaks, plants need to be supple as well as low; they bend before the blast instead of standing up against it. Woody plants are extremely rare on the heights. Those that manage to exist at all have such pliable branches that they can be twisted into all manner of shapes. Mountain specimens of the limber pine, which has an unmistakable tree form at lower elevations, are found growing flat on the ground. The Rocky Mountain snow willow is another ground-hugger, rising to a height of only an inch or two and yet managing to produce catkins in profusion. Though the snow willow has wholly lost its tree form, it is genetically related to lowland willows. After clambering over this plant on a mountaintop, whimsical botanists like to tell their friends, "I walked over a willow forest this morning."

LOWLANDERS tend to associate cold with snow. Actually snow is one of the great protectors and insulators in high mountains, and many plants take advantage of it. Temperatures on the surface of a snowbank may fall to zero or below, but underneath the snowbank the temperature rarely sinks to more than a few degrees below freezing. Furthermore, it stays consistently at that point and is not subjected to the wild gyrations found at the surface. In their alpine research area high in the Rockies, members of the University of Colorado's Arctic and Alpine Institute made some test borings in June through a 12-foot snowbank. At the bottom they found a tiny, exquisite snow buttercup in the process of opening its delicate yellow buds. How such seemingly fragile plants can live in such an environment is another of the marvels of mountain ecology.

To begin with, the snow buttercup, like other mountain flowers, is a slow and frugal grower. Although it will eventually need sunlight to produce the starches on which it depends for growth, it does not need them immediately. Consequently, if the snowbank under which it may start life fails to melt in any given year, it has the small but necessary resources to wait out the season until the next year.

The problem of cold does not bother this plant. As stated above, snow is a protection, not a hazard. The buttercup's cells are very small, and their fluid so rich in dissolved nutrients that it resists freezing just as an automobile's antifreeze does. Furthermore, its metabolic processes actually produce a very small quantity of heat, and this is apparently enough to start the plant growing in response to the triggering apparatus which tells

NORTH AMERICAN cushion-shaped pink (above) is a mountain-dwelling relative of the Indian pink below. Having adapted to harsh mountain climates, it looks like the unrelated South American cushion plant (opposite) rather than its own ancestor. This shows how dissimilar plants can become look-alikes on mountains.

it that spring has come, although present studies have not detected how, deep in the dark under the snow, the plant can do this.

When the snow begins to melt, it supplies a handy source of water, which is soaked up by the plant's elaborate root system, for like the cushion pink, the snow buttercup is mostly roots. As the covering snowbank becomes thinner and thinner, the plant actually begins to get a little energy from the sun, whose light can penetrate as much as a foot of snow. Finally it is uncovered to the open air, and its small leaf system must produce enough starch through photosynthesis during the few weeks of summer to carry the plant through the next winter—or perhaps several winters.

SOUTH AMERICAN plant (above), like the cushion pink (opposite), grows in a dense clump to survive on cold, windy heights. Its ancestral form was probably like the tall, spindly cow parsnip (below). This process, in which unrelated plants evolve until they resemble each other, is called "convergent evolution."

Plants like the snow buttercup live on a very small margin of safety. The energy required to produce leaves and flowers represents a high proportion of the total stored energy of the plant. Yet it must produce both if it is to grow and reproduce itself. As a consequence, many mountain plants must wait for three or four years, adding a bit to their energy hoard each year, until they have a large enough surplus to risk blooming. The glacier lily, after waiting seven years to flower, may be killed by the struggle to replace its leaves if an animal should eat them early in the spring. Careless picking of this plant by climbers almost invariably dooms it to death.

Many of the flowers found in alpine meadows are brilliantly colored, like the deep yellow of the snow buttercup or the intense dark blue of the gentian. Inasmuch as dark colors absorb light and heat, this would seem to be another useful adaptation of mountain plants. What is surprising is that there are so many pale-colored and white ones. The important thing is that the leaves of almost every alpine plant are dark green and highly heat-absorbent.

Leaves have other extremely ingenious adaptations. Many are thick and waxy, to resist evaporation. Others, like Switzerland's famed edelweiss, are coated with a thick fuzz of hairs, which not only trap heat but also resist the chilling effect of wind. Most interesting of all is the fuzz that grows on the pussy-willowlike buds of the snow willow. This fuzz is white, and at first glance it would seem to be a poor collector of heat. However, on closer examination, the core to which the hairs are attached is seen to be black. Light and heat penetrating the translucent surface of each hair are soaked up by the black bud, and then trapped there, for the hairs act like a miniature greenhouse, reflecting back into the interior all the heat that has been trapped.

Despite these adaptations, ingenious as they are, the plants that exploit them still must depend on some snow or rain, and a certain minimum fertility and stability in the soil. But these are not necessarily guaranteed in all mountain environments. Very little rain falls on the lee slopes of some mountain ranges, like the American Sierras. The winds blow steadily against their western flanks, depositing most of their moisture there, and producing in the "rain shadow" of those leeward slopes conditions which are as arid as those found in deserts. An extreme example of such disparity is Hawaii's Waialeale volcano. Its windward side receives some 465 inches of rain a year, a stupendous downpour that leaches the soil of nutrients and makes grass grow so fast that it absorbs very little of whatever nourishment may be left. A cow fed nothing but this watery grass would starve.

In contrast, the volcano's leeward side receives 20 inches annually and its sparse, desertlike vegetation is stunted.

At higher altitudes, of course, heavy precipitation is in the form of snow. Great concentrations of snow on steep slopes are unstable, and are the source of avalanches which can destroy in a few seconds large swaths of vegetation which may have been laboriously establishing themselves on mountainsides for decades. Large trees are carried away like matchsticks, and all manner of shrubs and bushes with them, often even the topsoil in which they grow. But even in the face of these major catastrophes certain plants are adapted to withstand the force of the rushing snow. The avalanche willow grows in a dense matted form, presenting such a slippery smooth surface that snow can slide over it several times in a single year without dislodging the plant itself.

But the stuff of mountains is an unstable footing for plants in other less obvious and more insidious ways. Simple gravity tends to pull downward everything that can be nudged loose. Heating by the sun, followed by freezing of water in their cracks, is constantly breaking up rocks. Pieces fall away, causing rockslides that uproot vegetation or bury it in debris. Once an area is scraped clean of its plant cover, it becomes subject to further weathering, since plants are the great stabilizers of the earth's surface. They tend to hold soil in place; they cover up the finer-ground grains and prevent them from being blown away by the wind; they temper the force of falling water by soaking it up and holding it, rather than letting it fall in a cutting torrent down a slope.

And while they hold soil, plants also create it. Their roots are constantly prying rocks apart, doing their small but steady bit in grinding up into smaller and smaller fragments the primordial slabs of which mountains are made. Lichens often grow incredibly slowly, one reason being that they can establish themselves in places where there is almost no water at all, and must make out with infinitesimal precipitations of dew. As a result, a small lichen patch a few inches across and perhaps one quarter of an inch high may be several hundred years old. And yet these obscure little plants are among the most important ever evolved. In such a minute fertile patch a moss may obtain a foothold, and from that, by slow degrees, an entire forest.

THE relationships of plants to soil are endlessly surprising. Most gardeners know that a "turning over" of earth and the aeration that goes with it are important, and they depend on earthworms to perform that function for them. But in the high mountains it is too cold for earthworms, and their function as disturbers and aerators of the soil is taken over by small burrowing animals. They become the gardeners of the tundra, with results which are often quite unexpected. Apparently driven to frenzy by overpopulation, a species of mouse called the meadow vole periodically

THE TUNNELING GOPHER kills grass in an alpine meadow not only by clawing and gnawing at roots but also by throwing soil to the surface where it will be blown away by the wind. The grass cannot survive in the remaining gravel, which is colonized by yarrow, campanulas and other plants (center) whose deeper roots can penetrate to the subsurface water. They are joined by cushion plants with deep taproots.

These cushions begin to catch dust and vegetable debris, and thus slowly build up a new stratum of soil (far right, below) in which the grasses can now take hold. The thick, shallow roots of the grasses begin to soak up all the surface water and the other plants die out, thus completing a cycle which may take as long as 100 years.

tears cushion plants and dwarf clover to shreds. The litter makes a good bed for such plants as mountain aven and mountain clover, which otherwise would not have such an easy time establishing themselves.

A common tundra sedge, *Kobresia*, is even more seriously affected by the excavations of the pocket gopher. As William Osburn of the University of Colorado explains it, *Kobresia* needs a fine deep humus soil. In such an environment it flourishes, along with certain cushion plants. Unfortunately, gophers are very fond of the cushion-plant roots, and in the course of their excavations one of these small rodents may throw up onto the surface of the ground several tons of soil in a year, smothering the individual plants. Strong winds eventually blow this soil away entirely, and *Kobresia* dies out, for it can no longer prosper in the gravelly soil that remains. The area begins to be colonized by a new type of vegetation—the lavender-clustered sky pilot, the white-flowered yarrow and the blue-flowered harebell, all of which grow high enough to withstand the piling up of dirt. But these plants are not to the gopher's taste and it moves on. Slowly the cushion plants creep back with their long taproots which can probe deep in the gravel for water. In their dense clusters they collect dust, and the decay of their bodies adds to the accumulation of a humus soil. Once more *Kobresia* is able to move in. When it does, it kills off the sky pilots, yarrows and most cushion plants, for its shallow, wide-spreading roots catch all the water that falls, and the cycle is completed.

So much for the rugged conditions with which mountain plants must cope. There still remains the larger question, how did they get there in the first place? This takes us into the complex realm of evolution and speciation, and introduces a fundamental concept of genetics: since most living things have slightly different genetic compositions, they will produce slightly different kinds of offspring. Those individuals which are best adapted to live in the areas in which they take root will prosper and produce others of their kind. But there is always the odd flower, the result of a mutation, that is a little different, one perhaps in a million or a billion normal flowers. As long as conditions remain unchanged, this odd flower will be handicapped in its struggle to exist alongside others of its species and will die out as fast as it appears. But if conditions should change even slightly, the "oddness" of the odd flower might turn out to be an advantage. Soon its type would predominate.

Mutations are alterations in the genetic structure of an organism. Although most of them appear to be spontaneous in origin, it is now known that they are brought about in several ways: by extremes of cold or heat, by chemicals or by oxygen deficiency. They are also caused when an organism's genes are struck by radiation and altered slightly. Since all of the above factors prevail with greater force on mountaintops than at sea level, the higher one goes the greater the potential for genetic change will be.

Taking all of these forces into consideration, it is not hard to visualize a situation in which a species of plant living at the foot of a mountain might gradually develop specialized varieties which were slightly more cold-resistant through being shorter-stemmed or fuzzier-leaved. These would tend to live at the upper limits of the normal flower's range, and might in turn produce even fuzzier types which could exist still higher. That a process somewhat akin to this actually does take place is evidenced by comparing a sunflower of the tundra with other, low-dwelling members of the sunflower family. They have enough structural characteristics in common to make it clear to botanists that they are closely related and are undoubtedly descended from a common ancestor, although to an untrained observer they might seem as different from one another as cabbages are from carrots.

ALL this is fine in theory, but there is a difficulty. There are at the tops of mountains species of plants which are not and, as far as botanists can tell, never have been closely related to lowland neighbors. Instead they are much more closely related to arctic species. In fact, the Rockies actually share 65 species of flowering plants with the North American arctic. How did *they* get there?

The force responsible for this paradox seems to be climatic change. There have been three ice ages in North America during the last million years, the most recent only 12,000 years ago, and the advance and retreat of the ice sheets may very well have been pushing all manner of growing things around at a greater rate than most people would ever imagine. Let us visualize what might have happened an indeterminate number of thousands of years ago, when the ice began to creep down from the north. This would affect the climate for hundreds of miles to the south, with increasing severity as the ice sheet grew. Some species of plants would be driven out by the drop in temperature. Others would be simply crushed by the ice. One after another the stands of existing timber would be overrun. Those that could reseed themselves rapidly would succeed in re-establishing themselves far to the south, in new belts of vegetation comparable to those that previously had existed in the north.

On the mountains, meanwhile, the ice would descend, driving the tundra plants farther and farther downslope until in some instances they were actually growing on the plains. Here they would stay until the ice sheet began to retreat. As it did, the tundra would move north again. When it encountered a mountain range, some of the tundra plants would find as attractive living space on the mountain's flanks as they might farther north on the flat. Eventually, with the climate steadily warming up and under pressure of other encroaching plants, the tundra-specialized species would find themselves where they are today, near the tops of temperate mountains.

In this sense, mountaintops are islands in a sea of moving vegetation and changing climate. That they are there now, and have been for an estimated 10,000 years, means nothing in the long surge of the earth's climate. If the average temperature of this continent were to rise by only a few degrees, the timber line on all our mountains would inexorably creep upward uptil it touched the tallest peaks. The tundra would vanish, its remarkable and specialized plants with it.

Plants on Mountains

The relationship of plants to their environment is nowhere more complex than in the mountains. Within a short distance each slope displays great variations in temperature, rainfall, wind and soil. Among these rigors, each plant settles where it is best suited and adapts itself to survival. Thus are formed the mountain-girdling bands of life shown on the following pages.

EDGING UP SHELTERED SLOPES, STANDS OF ENGELMANN SPRUCE AND SUBALPINE FIR LOSE SIZE PERCEPTIBLY AS THEY APPROACH

Trees at Timber Line

Cold and drought, the chief limiters of highland plant life, work most dramatically on the tree population. For lack of moisture and frost-free growing time, dense stands of pine and fir dwindle and thin out as they range up a slope. Finally, along the ragged timber line, the hardiest of alpine species fail to get their minimal needs and give way to shrubs, mosses and barren wastes.

Trees are not only dwarfed by the arid cold as they approach timber line, but also deformed by fierce prevailing winds. Some grow huddled over or even prostrate. Others grow no branches on their windward side (*opposite*). Still others have "wind-trained" branches circling their trunks, onto the leeward side. Over two miles up, most trees are gnarled and shrublike, and survive the winter only because they are protected by thick blankets of snow. Many a climber, thinking he has climbed above timber line in the snow, finds himself tangled in the treetops of an elfin forest, whose decades of growth may amount to no more than a dense mat of ground-clinging greenery.

APPARENTLY GROWING FROM ROCK, each of these trees (*left*) actually took root in a small pocket of moss or debris in a rock crack, and managed to survive and develop there.

TIMBER LINE IN COLORADO'S ROCKY MOUNTAINS. IN THIS REGION TREES SELDOM CAN SURVIVE ABOVE ELEVATIONS OF 11,500 FEET

WITHSTANDING THE ELEMENTS at timber line, a solitary fir puts most of its growth into a wide, thick mat of ground-level branches, which is completely covered and insulated by snow through the winter. Higher up on the trunk, the tree's branch buds on the windward side have been sheared off by sharp particles of ice whirling along in winter gales.

SENECIO

ALPINE

12,000

GIANT HEATH

ROCK HYRAX

HEATH

9,500

LEOPARD

BAMBOO

BAMBOO

7,500

TREE FERN

DUIKER

RAIN FOREST

5,500

FOREST BUFFALO

ELEPHANT

ACACIA TREE

SAVANNA

THE RUWENZORI HAS FIVE DISTINCT LIFE ZONES. THEIR AVERAGE ALTITUDES AND MAIN PLANTS AND ANIMALS ARE SHOWN ABOVE

The Mountains of the Moon

As a mountain gains altitude, its changes in environment are reflected in bandlike limitations on the distribution of plants and animals. On no mountains is this stratification of life more extreme or dramatic than on the Ruwenzori, a mist-shrouded range 80 miles long in equatorial Africa, known in ancient legend as "The Mountains of the Moon." Here, within a few miles, are jungle heat and glacial cold; and a world museum of living things is crowded into five distinct zones of habitation (*above*).

The range was not discovered by Europeans until 1888, when explorer Henry Stanley glimpsed snow-clad peaks during a rare break in the cloud cover. It was he who named the range Ruwenzori after a native word meaning "rain maker." Up to 350 days a year, a drizzling rain falls to feed the growth of Ruwenzori's gigantic foliage. Base level in this bizarre realm is the savanna (*opposite*), 5,500 feet high and teeming with animals. Human habitation ends around 6,700 feet in the fern-choked rain forest. Above rises the bamboo forest, and then the cold, dripping heath, largest region of its kind in the world, and the Alpine zone, where pioneer plants creep up windswept rock to the glaciers' edge. Though mountain climbers now follow well-marked trails, few parties have struggled all the way up through the deep bogs and suffocating verdure to scale the six 16,000-foot summits above the glaciers.

FROM THE SAVANNA, a high grassy plain (*opposite*) where elephants browse under acacia trees, Ruwenzori's foothills ascend into low-lying cloud banks and year-round rains.

94

IN THE RAIN FOREST, giant ferns (*left*) spread their fronds in a feathery canopy and wild banana trees are tangled with lianas. Girdling Ruwenzori from 5,500 to 7,500 feet, this zone is kept soaked by 150 inches of annual rainfall.

THE HEATH ZONE, starting at about 9,500 feet (*opposite*), is the domain of gnarled heather trees, lichen-fringed and drooping over beds of moss and liverwort. The trees are 40-foot relatives of the low brush on Scottish moors.

THE BAMBOO FOREST, slanting slender stalks over a trail (*below*) where porters rest, forms a dense belt between the rain forest and the heath. A kind of grass, bamboo may grow three feet a day and reach 100 feet in two months.

SCALY TRUNK of a tree senecio, gigantic member of the aster family, grows to a rosette of cabbagelike leaves and a flowering spike. At lower right is a carex tussock. Both plants are dominant in the Alpine zone but also inhabit the heath's upper reaches.

MISTY BORDERLAND of the heath and Alpine zones at 12,000 feet (*left*) is a cold morass strewn with fallen trees, carpeted with yellow and orange moss. Tall heathers and lobelia spikes loom up in a drizzling fog which blots out the sun and muffles sound.

ABOVE 12,000 FEET, black lichens and brown mosses pioneer the bleak Alpine zone near a glacial lake. Lichens create seedbeds for more advanced flower-bearing plants.

STORM-SWEPT ICE grips a pinnacle (*opposite*), jutting up toward one of Ruwenzori's six towering summits. The range is wrapped in permanent snow above 14,500 feet.

OVERLAPPING PETALS of a mountain laurel trigger off a puff of pollen which dusts any insect that lands on them—an important device in mountains, where insects are rare.

SMALL AND SHORT-STEMMED, the cushion pink nestles in a sheltered hollow, using its energy to grow the dense flower clusters and three-foot taproots it needs to survive.

Ingenious Adaptations for the Heights

Though closely related to lowland plants, the true alpine plants shown on these pages are distinct species, having as their chief characteristics the ingenious mechanisms by which they adapt to the bitter conditions of the high mountainside.

Certainly the most conspicuous of these adaptations is small size, often including very short stems, which permits many alpine plants to lie low, out of the wind's way, and to concentrate the little growth they are capable of in their

BELL-BLOOMED STALKS OF ALPINE SOLDANELLA MELT THEIR WAY UP THROUGH THE SNOW BY RADIATING STORED ENERGY AS HEAT

FURRY SURFACES of leaves and stems help strawflowers survive by retarding their transpiration, thus conserving precious moisture quickly lost to the dry alpine winds.

INTENSE COLOR of the purple gentian is a characteristic which many plants develop at high altitudes. Scientists speculate that this kind of coloration attracts certain insects.

short growing season into the blooms they need to reproduce, and into the long roots they need to collect moisture in the thin, dry soil. To conserve moisture, some plants grow thick fuzz or a waxy film on their leaves. Another kind of economy is the "evergreen habit," which lets a species use one set of hard-earned leaves for more than one season. Some plants are so well adapted to cold and to a minimum of sunlight that they start growing while buried under a snowbank.

DWARFED BY A DIME, THE BLOOMS OF A PYGMY RANUNCULUS SURVIVE ON MOISTURE CONSERVED BY THE WAX COATING ITS LEAVES

FLAMING ROCKS in a Colorado pass (*opposite*) are encrusted with brilliant red, yellow and orange lichens. Usually the first plant to appear on barren ground, the lichen is really two plants coexisting as one: a fungus, whose acids break down rock into soil, and an alga, which supplies organic matter that the fungus needs to survive.

"WATERMELON" SNOW along a brook in Colorado's Rockies (*below*) owes its characteristic tint and scent to invisible tiny algae which secrete a red gelatinous covering for protection. The most primitive of plants, the alga is so insensitive to extreme temperatures that some species can survive for months while frozen in a block of ice.

WELL INSULATED against the thin, frigid air of the Andes by their woolly coats, guanacos are also specialized for high-mountain living by remarkably efficient oxygen utilization in their blood stream.

5

Denizens
of the Slopes

THE tenacity of the world's hardiest perennials, clinging to their crannies on the alpine heights, compels a kind of admiration. And yet it is entirely understandable, since a plant will have to grow wherever its seed may fall and germinate, be it a mountain crag or a sidewalk crack. With animal life it is a different story. Where the plants are passive the animals are active, mobile, able to pick up and leave when they encounter danger or mere unpleasantness. They have some choice—and yet an astounding variety and number of them persist in living in what is unquestionably one of the most difficult environments on earth. Every factor that makes life rugged for the plants works against the animals too, and more besides. They must endure the same wind, the cold, the extremes of temperature and flood and aridity, the insubstantial soil, the treacheries of ice and snow. Somehow they must also get oxygen out of the rarefied air, and find food and drink on terrain so steep that it allows no false step.

What gets animals to the heights in the first place? There are many reasons, some obvious, some still unfathomed. Insects may have no more choice in the matter than plant seeds, being carried up by rising winds.

THE AMERICAN ELK, one of a number of horned animals that live on mountains, carries a handsome rack of antlers which may measure 60 inches from tip to tip. Of the four mountain dwellers pictured here, the elk is by far the largest.

THE ALPINE CHAMOIS has round, short horns that rise straight from the animal's head, then abruptly hook backward. A small, delicate-looking animal weighing only about 65 pounds, the chamois is extremely elusive on high mountain slopes.

But most high-mountain mammals and birds are almost certainly fugitives —either seasonal or permanent—from stiff competition for food and life in the crowded lowlands. Whether hungry or hunted by predators, they have simply taken to the hills. What has happened to them since they got there might be surprising to a man who has studied only plants and knows of the extraordinary evolutionary changes that have been wrought in species like the cushion pink. If he had never seen a mountain animal at all, he might be tempted to try and design one.

One or two things would occur to him immediately: the animal would have to eat; therefore it would have to be able to move around sufficiently to browse on the available plant life. But mountains are cold, and plant life is scarce, and we have already seen that if it is browsed too heavily it will die. So, a designer's first conclusion, and it would be a correct one, might be that the number of animals on mountains must be relatively low and that they will have to be able to keep warm.

IDEALLY, the animal that could keep the warmest would be a ball-shaped creature with short legs, diminutive ears and a thick coat. This configuration is obviously suitable because a sphere contains a greater amount of volume in proportion to its surface than any other solid shape. And since animals lose heat through their skins, a spherical animal would be the most efficient. Furthermore, a large sphere is better in that respect than a small one. A one-inch marble has three square inches of surface and about half a cubic inch of volume, whereas a one-foot cannon ball has 452 square inches of surface and 904 cubic inches of volume—12 times as much in proportion as the marble.

So our scientist, blueprint in hand, might well start up into the mountain, full of confidence that he will find a quantity of large "schmoo"-shaped animals, preferably black ones since dark colors absorb heat more readily than light. After prolonged search he may find a few creatures that vaguely approach that form, but there will be so many others of radically different appearance that he will certainly hurry down again and go back to his drawing board with a red face.

What has gone wrong with his calculations? In the first place, although mountains are certainly bitterly cold, they are not always so; sometimes at midday in protected areas they get hotter than the plains. Obviously a large fuzz-ball would suffer terribly in such a variable climate unless it had some mechanism for cooling off. In addition, its roly-poly shape would not help it in escaping predators, and we may be sure that meat eaters would follow the plant eaters up the mountains. For survival, some of them, at least, would have to be able to run fairly fast.

Mobility, next to the inability to manufacture its own food, is certainly the most important characteristic that separates animals from plants, and one which has made it possible for a wide variety of animals to make the adjustments necessary for life in the mountains without drastic changes in their particular lowland form. Living conditions vary from season to season on a mountain, even from hour to hour and from place to place. A small sheltered nook in a mountain cleft may be totally different from an exposed outcrop a dozen feet away. For plants, which are anchored for life, adaptation is essential. For animals, which can move, it is not so important.

But size is. A very small mammal will lose heat so rapidly through its relatively large skin surface that it must keep furiously active and its own internal furnace must be continuously stoked with fuel or it will freeze to death. The mountain shrew, which is the smallest mammal found at high altitudes, has a tremendously high body metabolism; it must burn up its own stored energy at a prodigious rate simply to keep warm. Its heart beats up to 1,200 times a minute, it must find something to eat at least every hour, and must consume its own weight in food every day or it will die. Some shrews in captivity have been known to eat as much as three times their own weight in a day. It follows that warm-blooded animals tend to attain their maximum size in cold climates.

There are three principal ways in which warm-blooded animals can deal with the problem of cold on mountains: through migration, through hibernation, or by seeking shelter under the ground or under the snow.

Most large mountain animals migrate. In the American Rockies, elk and bighorn sheep, which browse on the heights during the summer, begin to drift downward in late autumn to avoid the deep snows. They spend the winter below timber line in protected thickets, where they can obtain food, or from which they can move out onto wind-blown open meadows for forage. They avoid the worst of the cold by staying out of the wind and by growing thick winter coats. With the coming of spring they move upward again. As the snows melt and tender willow shoots begin to sprout, they follow the season, lured always higher by the promise of a continuing supply of fresher, tenderer young shoots a few hundred feet farther up. This protects the willows themselves against overgrazing.

Predators will follow them, of course, the principal one being the mountain lion. Known also as the cougar, panther, puma or catamount, this is the largest carnivore common to North America. Once it roamed the entire continent, but today it is largely a mountain species, partly because of relentless hunting by man and partly because man has also hunted to near extermination many of the animals the mountain lion lives on. Generations of American children have grown up in fear of this huge cat with its unearthly scream in the night. Certainly it is an impressive animal, of marvelous grace, stealth and strength, sometimes growing to 200 pounds, but the reputation it has as an attacker of man is greatly exaggerated. One did kill and eat a 13-year-old boy in Washington state in 1924, but that is the only such occurrence on record, and most naturalists are convinced that the few instances of cougars molesting people are the result of the cougars' suffering from rabies. Ordinarily they are merely curious about man, and may trail a woodsman or trapper for miles through the forest, although he will almost never be aware of it.

THE mountain lion is a fine natural regulator of deer, which tend to become too numerous and ruin forests by overbrowsing if natural predators are not present to keep their numbers within healthy limits. It also can pull down elk, though the latter may run as high as 1,200 pounds in weight, and it will take its share of bighorn sheep if it can get close enough to them. The sheep are extraordinarily sharp-eyed and sure-footed, and unless they are out in the open in the upland meadows they are almost impossible to catch.

Oddly enough, the bighorn's greatest natural enemy is neither man nor mountain lion, but a tiny parasitic worm which invades its lungs. Animals

BIGHORN SHEEP are about twice the size of domestic sheep and the adult male has a pair of thick, curling horns. Like males of the other species shown on these pages, they use their horns chiefly to battle during mating season.

ROCKY MOUNTAIN GOATS are not goats at all but members of the chamois family. Both sexes have black, daggerlike horns which they will use, if pressed, to fight a predator, but they normally use their climbing ability to evade enemies.

so infected become scrawny and run-down, and many of them are cleaned off by predators before they can be killed by the worm. Scientists did not understand the nature of this ailment for a while, since sheep in certain areas were entirely free of it whereas those in others were heavily ravaged. They finally traced the trouble to a small mountain snail in whose body the worm must spend part of its life cycle before it can attack the sheep. But snails can live only in certain areas because they need lime to manufacture their shells. Thus, sheep living in mountains made of granite are usually free of the disease, whereas those living in areas where the soil contains lime are apt to be infected.

Large mountain herbivores are all sure-footed. They have independently developed a similar type of hoof which enables them to travel at great speed over rough rocky ground, and also to traverse steep ledges without losing their footing. The hoofs of these animals are flexible, with pincerlike toes, and they also have relatively soft, arched bottoms which give them excellent traction on steep rocky surfaces. A wolf, for example, can seldom catch a bighorn sheep in rough uplands, but with the construction of smooth black-top roads in much mountain country a new hazard has been introduced for the bighorn. It occasionally likes to bed down on such roads, presumably because their dark surfaces soak up heat, and a wolf, suddenly coming around a corner, can often catch a bighorn before it can scramble to safety.

Wariness and speed are essential to this animal if it is to survive. Consequently, lambs must be, and in fact they are, precocious from birth. Within an hour of its birth a lamb can stand up to suckle. Within a week it can follow its mother wherever she goes. Within two weeks it can run as fast as she can. Bighorn ewes and lambs bleat back and forth much like domestic sheep; rams are silent except to snort-sneeze a signal of danger, and grind their teeth in anger.

THE enormous horns of the ram are among the most remarkable in the animal kingdom. They grow in a continuous curve and in old males will actually come full circle, sometimes a circle and a half. They are not weapons in the conventional sense. Among males their principal function seems to be to establish superiority over other males during the mating season by engaging in spectacular butting duels. The combatants first rear and slash at each other with their sharp front hoofs, then turn back to back and stalk away from each other like human duelists. Turning and rearing once more, they then charge at top speed to meet head-on with a crash that can be heard a mile or two away. Dazedly, they walk off and repeat the procedure. The battle may be ended after a couple of passes, or it may go on for two hours and leave both contestants bruised and bloody. Once in a great while a skull is fractured or a horn irreplaceably broken, or a contestant butted over a cliff.

Interestingly enough, the hair of the bighorn sheep is straight, like that of a deer. The dense wool commonly associated with sheep is a result of selective breeding in domesticated strains. Nevertheless bighorns have heavy enough coats to withstand sub-zero temperature. They never seem to suffer from the cold unless their food supply is cut off by heavy snow and they begin to starve.

Many smaller animals deal with extreme cold by hibernating. The idea here might almost be expressed as: if you can't beat the cold, join it. In other words, find an underground burrow where it is not too cold, then allow your own body temperature to sink down until it is almost as low as that of the surrounding air. From then on, the body will suffer no further heat loss, and if you can survive at that low temperature everything will be all right.

That is exactly what hibernation is. A ground squirrel, having gorged itself on food during the summer and autumn months, will be as fat as butter. Then it retires to its burrow which, lined with grasses or hairs from its own body, will tend to be a fairly snug spot with a temperature of 45 or 50 degrees. The squirrel then falls into a deep sleep, its bodily functions slow down and its temperature gradually drops to the low 50s also. In this comatose state, it will use up its stored energy very slowly. The heartbeat of the ground squirrel is reduced in hibernation from a normal 200 beats per minute to as low as 20 beats per minute, and it will wake up again in the spring, hungry and perhaps even a bit thin, but otherwise in perfect condition.

WHAT is more surprising is that there is a bustle of small animal life in the high mountains the year round. Rodents are the commonest of mountain mammals, and many of them are active throughout the winter. They find protection, as do many mountain plants, under the snow, where it never gets so cold that they cannot function comfortably. Perhaps the most numerous of all alpine rodents is the meadow vole. Lively specimens were dug out of a snowbank one icy winter day by biologists on a Colorado mountainside, and they froze to death in two or three minutes. But down in their labyrinthine burrows, under the warming cover of the snow itself, they prosper mightily.

MOUNTAIN HAYMAKER, the pika, prepares a store of grass and flowers which it dries in small piles among the rocks. The kitten-sized animal does not hibernate and depends entirely upon its hay reserves throughout the winter months.

Small rodents are the food staple of a great many predators. Eagles, hawks, foxes, weasels, all take their toll, and the vole's defense is in an overwhelming fecundity. A female vole becomes sexually mature at five weeks, and thereafter may deliver litters of up to eight offspring every three weeks. Clearly no fox can eat that many voles, or even breed enough cubs to do the job. As a result the voles would live in constant danger of self-extermination through overpopulation if they were not subject to an extraordinary regulator. Periodically they go through what are known as population collapses. The number of voles in a given area will build up very rapidly. Then, quite suddenly, instead of going about their regular business of eating and breeding, the voles will become nervous and agitated and will spend most of their time wildly shredding grasses and sedges. Breeding is forgotten and, since the life expectancy of the vole is just under one year on the average, in a very short time the population will drop to less than one per cent of what it has been a few months previously.

Several theories have been advanced to explain this phenomenon. One postulates that the voles have consumed all the available supply of an as-yet-undetermined plant or plants which furnish an ingredient critical to the vole's diet, and that its wild behavior is induced by desperation, and its death by its being unable to get enough of this substance, whatever it may be. Another theory suggests that simple crowding frazzles the voles' nerves. Experimental animals kept in cages begin to show signs of nervous strain when their population reaches a certain critical point, even

though their diet has been and continues to be adequate. Strength is given to this theory by introducing a tranquilizer into the diet; tranquilized voles will continue to breed until the cage is almost literally filled solid with tiny vole bodies.

By contrast, the populations of ground squirrels, pocket gophers, rock marmots and many other small mountain mammals are more stable. The pika, a small, short-eared, tailless relative of the rabbit, suffers neither population collapse nor does it hibernate. It is the haymaker of the mountains. It spends the summer months busily cutting grasses and weeds, which it spreads in protected places among rocks in small piles. Popular legend has it that the pika hastily "gets its hay in" like a farmer whenever a rainstorm threatens. But this is not so. Grasses dry so rapidly in the thin air and hot sun of the mountains that occasional rains cannot spoil them. In a snug, grass-lined nest surrounded by handy hay piles, the pika gets through the winter very well.

MANY of these small mammals have gone a certain distance, if not all the way, in approaching the fuzzy-ball shape that a hypothetical animal designer might have figured out as best for them. They are short-legged and small-eared and, furthermore, they can make themselves round. They curl up in balls when they hibernate or sleep. This not only conserves body heat, but it tends to protect the spot from which many animals lose heat: the belly, where the hair is usually thin and fine. On warm days a marmot will cool itself by stretching out in the breeze, or lie with its sparsely covered belly in a patch of snow.

A snowshoe rabbit, huddled at rest, its feet tucked under it, its ears back, looks like an almost perfect furry ball. It can sit motionless in the snow for hours without getting cold, and the lower the temperature gets the more it will fluff up its fur and the rounder it will become. Yet it is a slender creature with long legs. When chased, and under the necessity of losing heat from a body metabolism which may suddenly shoot up to 20 times what it is when the animal is sitting still, its shape will be so drastically altered that it can run at top speed for considerable distances if necessary without collapsing from heat exhaustion.

Rabbits and hares show other adaptations to mountain living. In the deserts of Arizona, the jack rabbit has enormous, sparsely haired ears which average nearly one fourth its total body length—a helpful specialization in keeping the animal cool in a hot climate, but not necessary for jack rabbits of the Northwest, whose ears are only a fifth as long as their bodies. The ears of the snowshoe rabbit are little more than one eighth of its body length—and those of the arctic hare are even smaller. In addition the ears of these northern species are heavily furred on their outer surfaces.

The proper name of the snowshoe rabbit is the varying hare, and it gets this name because its color varies with the seasons. In summer it is brown, for better camouflage, but in fall white patches begin to appear on it, and in a few weeks it is entirely white, to blend with the snow. This might seem to put the hare at a disadvantage in the matter of heat storage, since a white coat will soak up less external heat than a dark one. However, it also prevents loss of heat from the animal itself, by reflecting back toward its skin a good deal of what is emitted. For this reason, the best

A FAT ROCKCHUCK, or marmot, scurries toward an underground den as a golden eagle swoops down. This eagle nests high in inaccessible cliffs and constantly preys on marmots. The marmots protect themselves by living on rocky slopes which provide many small crevices in which to dig burrows or find temporary shelter from surprise attacks. They also warn each other of danger by whistling.

hairs for very cold weather would theoretically be dark at their tips, but white where they enter the animal's body. However, science has learned little so far about the relationship of hair color to heat conservation—beyond the fact that it is a complex matter. The Himalayan rabbit, for example, appears to combine the best of both worlds—it has a white body with black ears, tail and feet. But laboratory experiments with this animal have revealed some strange facts which touch on the mystery and delicacy of the mechanisms which control hair color. When white hairs are plucked from it at a room temperature of 68 degrees or higher they grow back white, but if the temperature is kept below 50 degrees they come in black. Conversely, when black hairs are plucked and the bare patch kept warm with a bandage, they grow back white. This might be understandable if the rabbit itself were to change color in the natural state—but it does not and the experimenters still do not understand why.

One mammal that follows none of the rules mentioned so far is the Rocky Mountain goat, not a true goat but a member of the family that includes the chamois and stands midway between goats and antelopes. It does not hibernate, it does not migrate, it does not live under snowbanks. Rather, it spends its entire life in the rocks above timber line. Here again, however, can be traced interesting close relationships to lowland forms, which suggests that the mountain goats have merely made the most of certain specializations possessed by goats and antelopes the world over.

THEY are agile and sure-footed. They are also among the most efficient plant scavengers known. They make a comfortable living from the sparsest forage in arid lands where few other forms can do as well. A goat has four stomachs and by thoroughly working over the twigs and shrubs it does manage to find, it extracts the last possible bits of nourishment from them. This stands the mountain goat in good stead, for tundra forage, although extremely nourishing, is hard to find when deep snow blankets the peaks. Cold does not bother this animal. It has a short woolly undercoat and also grows a conspicuously thick shaggy outer coat, which hangs down far enough on its flanks to protect the barer portions of its belly. In summer, this extra hair falls off in handfuls, often giving the animal a most unkempt, patchy look. It is adept at finding shady spots in hot weather and will often dig into snowbanks to cool off. Furthermore, it seldom exerts itself. Over-heating being a direct result of rushing about, the goat very sensibly has adopted a leisurely way of life. It is wary enough, and likes to station itself on an exposed outcropping from which its keen eyes can survey the surrounding terrain for a considerable distance. A man climbing up into its domain will see a goat standing unconcernedly a quarter of a mile away, but when he puffs his way over an intervening ridge or two, the goat will still be a quarter of a mile away. The only way to get close to these animals is to get above them without being seen. When so encountered, they appear remarkably unconcerned, although one that was cornered by a naturalist on a cliff turned and butted him off into space—where fortunately he landed on an outcrop 10 feet below.

Mountain goats are among the most sure-footed of all mountain creatures. They venture along ledges which are so narrow as to appear impassable. Occasionally, when a ledge peters out to nothing, a goat, unable to back up, will very carefully rear up on its hind legs, turn around facing the cliff, and unconcernedly walk out again. Although stocky animals, their bodies are deep rather than plump, and this facilitates movement on rock ledges. The only thing that they seem vulnerable to is sudden large falls of snow or rock; there is evidence that a good many are killed by avalanches.

Goats of various kinds live in most of the mountains of the world, and their habits are quite similar, although in appearance they vary considerably. The European ibex is the most conspicuous example, being the possessor of magnificent ridged horns which sometimes grow half as long as the animal itself. By contrast, the horns of the Rocky Mountain goat are small and spiky. However, they are extremely sharp, and hard-pressed goats have been known to drive off and even kill hungry grizzly bears. All in all, they are the most admirably adapted of all mammals to the heights, and they share their lonely eminences the year round with certain insects and spiders and a few hardy birds like ptarmigan and ravens—which come up to its level during mild winter weather.

Of all creatures, birds are the best adapted to mountain living since they are the most mobile. Eagles and vultures haunt the crags, small animals being the usual prey of the former and carrion that of the latter. In each case structure has become all-important. The largest member of the vulture family, the Andean condor is an almost perfect glider. It is an enormous bird, with a wingspread of up to 10 feet, but its bones are hollow and very light, and although about the same size as an emperor penguin, it weighs less than half as much. So equipped, it can effortlessly glide back and forth on the currents of air that rise up along all mountain ranges, depending on a pair of the world's keenest eyes to spot a dead rabbit or the carcass of a deer that a mountain lion may have abandoned as much as five miles away. It was once thought that vultures located carrion at great distances by a keen sense of smell, but experiments performed with carefully constructed models of small animals have proved that sight, as in eagles, is the important sense. The ornithologist Edward Howe Forbush once spotted a bald eagle with wings set, coasting by far above his head. He followed it with his binoculars, as it traveled, straight as an arrow, to land on a beach a mile and a half away to pick up a small dead fish.

Abrupt changes in altitude seem to have little effect on birds. An eagle can ride an updraft of warm air from a valley floor, spiraling in slow circles until it may have risen vertically by a matter of miles in half an hour. Such a sudden change would induce all manner of uncomfortable symptoms in a man since his lungs would be unable to take in sufficient oxygen in the thin air to give his system what it needed. But birds have more efficient lungs than men. They are larger in proportion, and they are so constructed as to bring a greater supply of oxygen into rapid contact with the blood. It may be argued that the eagle is simply soaring, letting the rising air currents do the work, and therefore needs no more oxygen than it might need sitting on top of a tree. But what of the bar-headed goose, a heavy bird which has been observed flying with strong wingbeats over the Himalayas at altitudes actually higher than the top of Everest? The energy requirements of this bird under these conditions are very great, and its circulatory and breathing apparatus must be of an efficiency unparalleled among mammals.

Far smaller than the condor, eagle or goose, but also closely associated with the heights, are swifts. Each continent has its members of this swallow-like family, an outstanding example being North America's black swift. This bird spends almost its entire life in the air, riding the updrafts all day long in a display of aerial ability that is unmatched in the bird world. Swifts have been clocked in dives at speeds in excess of 200 miles an hour. They feed on the wing, having wide mouths edged with stiff hairs, which are efficient catchers of the clouds of insects which are blown up from the valleys. They nest on ledges, and in fact must do so, since their feet are so weak that they cannot push themselves into the air from a sitting position, but must literally drop from a clinging perch in order to become air-borne. In winter, when the supply of flying insects disappears, the swifts migrate, some of them for thousands of miles to similar precipice environments in other continents.

Insects get to the mountains in quantities only in spring and summer. Once there, they are quickly numbed by the cold and drop on the snow. This does not necessarily kill them, it merely immobilizes them, for they belong to a large group of creatures which have no internal mechanism to regulate body temperature, and so take on the approximate temperature of their surroundings. Creatures having this characteristic are called poikilothermous, and include fish, reptiles and amphibians as well as insects. They are among the most numerous as well as the most primitive of life forms. Of the million-odd kinds of animals on earth, all but about 20,000 are poikilothermous.

In general, the lower an animal is on the evolutionary scale, the greater is its resistance to extremes of temperature. Depending on other circumstances, a human being will die if his temperature drops to about 65 or rises to about 112 degrees. But fish have been subjected to temperatures of -4 degrees, frogs to -18, a moth pupa to -31 and land snails to -184. Warmed up gradually and carefully, all survived. This is not to say that any of these animals can be frozen solid, however. If temperatures are low enough and are sustained long enough to permit ice crystals to form within the individual cells of an animal, those cells will die. Convincing demonstrations have been made by performers on the stage, aimed at showing that fish can be frozen solid, but they are fraudulent. The common practice is to drop a small goldfish into a container of liquid air, which quickly freezes the fish. A moment later a larger fish is dropped in, almost immediately withdrawn and placed in a jar of water, where it is seen to swim around apparently unharmed. Whereupon the small fish is removed from the liquid air and dramatically smashed to fragments with a hammer. What the audience does not realize is that the larger fish is also doomed. It will die in a day or two, since its skin and other cells of its outer tissues have been damaged by their momentary immersion in liquid air, and will fall off.

So long as the cellular fluid of many lower animals can resist freezing (and some of these fluids are remarkably resistant), there is nothing damaging per se about cold. All it does is restrict activity and sometimes habits. On mountain heights, with their drastic swings of temperature between day and night, insects that would normally fly or crawl abroad at night in the lowlands would be immobilized by the cold. As a result, most of them are absent at high altitudes although there are a few that have managed to adapt themselves by becoming creatures of the day. At night

AN UNDERWATER FORAGER, the water ouzel, or dipper, searches for food along the rocky bottoms of mountain streams. Several varieties live in mountain areas from Alaska to Central Asia and dive in swift, unfrozen streams all winter, even when the air is 50 degrees below zero.

they take shelter in the warm ground or in rock cracks and crevices, and simply lie dormant until returning warmth revives them. Even on days that are merely cloudy, bumblebees and flies become earth-bound; they walk dazedly about, or even lie torpid on their sides. Wolf spiders and other small predators including shrews find their best hunting in late afternoon when flying insects are unable to get about. As a counter to the cold, many alpine beetles are black, which enables them to soak up whatever sunlight there is with maximum efficiency. As a counter to the ever-present winds, certain butterflies habitually do their flying very close to the ground; if they flew higher they might be blown out of their ranges to altitudes with even more severe winds and more difficult living conditions. Other mountain insects have short wings, some have no wings at all.

Because of the problems imposed by wind and cold, it was long thought that most winged insects found on mountains were wind-blown, accidental arrivals. Gradually, however, it has been learned that some forms exist the year round, that there are butterflies which take two years to mature, and grasshoppers that may take three. But although certain insects eat other insects, all are ultimately dependent on plants, and the conviction was widespread for many years that at levels beyond which no plants grow, no insect can exist.

Imagine, then, the surprise of British climbers who found jumping spiders at 22,000 feet on Mount Everest. Were they wind-blown? If not, what insects did they eat, and what did *those* insects eat? The would-be scalers of Everest had neither the time nor the energy to seek an answer to this question, but a British naturalist, Major R.W.G. Hingston, suggested that other wind-blown spiders and insects provided them with food. In 1961 a more refined explanation was offered by an American biologist, Lawrence W. Swan, in an article published in *Scientific American*. Swan reconfirmed the existence of jumping spiders at many levels high in the Himalayas, and discovered what they ate—small flies and springtails. These insects in turn were found to live on fungi and rotting vegetation. What fascinated Swan was the discovery of springtails and glacier fleas higher up at levels where "there was no visible indication of plants past or present."

Neither springtail nor glacier flea can fly; the best either can manage is a short jump of an inch or so. It was clearly impossible to account for the presence of either species in those regions of bare, bitter, wind-swept rock and snow, except by conceding that they somehow managed to live there all the time. The glacier flea's adaptation for living under conditions of extreme cold was quickly worked out: it is a dark brown in color, and although it may spend the night frozen fast to a crust of snow, its dark body captures enough heat from the sun during the day to thaw the surrounding ice, letting the insect wriggle free and begin jumping about. But what did it eat? Careful search finally revealed a few dead insects in the snow and here and there tiny collections of wind-blown pollen. From this Swan concluded that minute insects and other forms can be considered year-round residents even of these incredible heights, and that "in the fastness of the Himalayas . . . there is a new ecological system to be explored; the supra-alpine or aeolian community, sustained by wind-blown debris." Life, which is now known to exist at the very bottom of the sea, presumably also exists in one form or another at the topmost peaks of the world.

LONG-HAIRED SNOW LEOPARD PROWLS THE MOUNTAINS OF CENTRAL ASIA, RARELY COMING BELOW 6,000 FEET EVEN IN WINTER

Fugitives from the Plains

The bare ridges and ravines of mountain terrain above timber line are not as desolate as they may look. A variety of animals abounds. Most are fugitives from the plains, forced to flee upward by competition with other animals. Many have become uniquely adapted to extremes of temperature and to scarcity of food and oxygen, rigors that go together with high altitude.

A VERSATILE CLIMBER, the aoudad of northwest Africa is equally at home on high crags in the Atlas Mountains and in the sun-baked Sahara. It is Africa's only wild sheep.

Adaptations of Pelt and Hoof

Wild goats and sheep seem ideally adapted for coping with the extremes of life above timber line. Able to make unusually efficient use of food, these animals are also careful conservers of energy, moving rapidly only when forced to by imminent danger. To counter the damp, cold climate of the heights, the Rocky Mountain goat (*opposite*) sports two water-repellent coats of hair, a long outer coat and a thick inner one. Best adaptations of all are hoofs made for quick travel over rough terrain. These are heeled with soft concave pads, which cling to steep surfaces like rubber, and have sharp cloven rims, which grip rock slopes almost like pincers. On such hoofs bighorns are able to descend nearly vertical inclines in a running series of 20-foot bounds.

COCKING ITS HEAD, a Rocky Mountain goat pauses in its search for forage above the timber line (*opposite*). Its slab-sided shape is ideal for travel along narrow ledges.

RUTTING BATTLE between Rocky Mountain bighorn rams begins as the two rear back to charge (*top*), proceeds to a head-on collision that leaves both animals dizzy (*bottom*).

119

The Return of the Ibex

Throughout the Alps today there are numerous herds of the magnificently horned ibexes. The tourist may now see scores of these animals feeding and sunning in steep meadows on high ridges. It was not always so. Just over a hundred years ago, the ibex, so long established in the Alps—cave men often depicted it in their paintings—was on the verge of total extinction. Ruthlessly hunted as game, the ibex was also sought and killed for its supposed medicinal value until by 1850 only a few remained on remote peaks in the Italian Alps. Then, King Victor Emmanuel II declared himself protector of the ibex, and a long comeback period for the animal began. In 1911 a successful attempt was made to introduce two males and three females into Switzerland, and today 2,000 descendants of these animals roam the Swiss Alps. The ibex seems assured of survival.

SCRATCHING ITS BACK, an ibex finds a handy use for its three-foot horns. These lengthen as the animal matures, building up in yearly growth rings not visible here. The prominent ridges are not considered a good index of age since the animal frequently adds two or three a year. In old individuals the ridges wear down to almost nothing.

MAJESTIC RAMS, their horns deeply chiseled by the morning light, amble along an upland pasture. Old males with prize spreads are at center; young males with short horns are in the foreground. Males customarily keep to the heights, consorting with females only during the mating season. Females and young herd together on the lower slopes.

A SHY GUANACO, a New World relative of the camel, stands sentinel for its browsing companions on an Andean ridge. Its domesticated descendants, the llama and alpaca, are the mainstays of South America's Indians, providing wool, meat and transport.

A PINK HOST of rare James's flamingos (*right*) nests along the mist-blue banks of a salt lake, 14,800 feet up in the Bolivian Andes. At this altitude flamingo fledglings must survive temperatures from 70 degrees during the day to five degrees above zero at night.

A LEGENDARY MARAUDER of many names, the mountain lion (*opposite*) is also known as puma, cougar and catamount. Though relentlessly hunted because it attacks livestock, it is the New World's most widely distributed large predator, ranging from Alaska to Argentina.

A TIMID HOME LOVER, the pika seldom ventures more than 30 feet away from its rockslide lair. Born in the spring, in litters of three to six, by fall its young have established their own nearby homesteads and gathered the stocks of hay that will see them through the winter.

FURTIVELY PEEPING from a crevice, a pair of golden-mantled squirrels (*below*) keep watch for predators. During the short mountain summer these rodents survive the onslaught of pumas, coyotes, hawks and weasels and get fat enough to be able to hibernate five to seven months.

SUDDEN DEATH comes to a ground squirrel (*right*) in the huge talons of a golden eagle, North America's largest predatory bird. Legend has it that the eagle steals children, but this is patently impossible: the bird cannot carry more than eight pounds in flight.

CLAMORING FOR FOOD, two nestling water ouzels (*below*) gape from a mossy nest in a Rocky Mountain cliff. As adults, they have a thick, oily plumage that enables them to walk along the sandy bottoms of icy mountain streams seeking insect larvae and snails.

6

Man at High Altitude

Mountains have molded man and shaped the course of much of his world's history. Often their massive bulk has deflected him, and sometimes their icy heights have deterred and defeated him. On occasion the mountains have been a refuge for him; always they have been a challenge. "Bring me men to match my mountains," says the inscription on one of the state buildings at Sacramento, California. A little more than a century ago, Sacramento was the center of modern man's most famous mass move to the mountains, the gold rush of Forty-nine. The gold in those hills has long since been gouged out, and the high slopes of the Sierra Nevada are in places a landscape of ghost towns. But Californians are still matching themselves against their mountains—and being molded by them. For it is the melting snow of the mountains, dammed and piped across the lowlands, that has turned their coastal desert into a garden and California into the most populous of the American states.

From this it might appear that when free to choose, and with the possibilities of self-advancement before them, men will tap the wealth of the mountains—their minerals, their waters, their forests, their possibilities for tourism—but they will not live there. This seems to be true for such new lands as the American West, the Canadian Rockies and the New Zealand Alps. But it is only a part of the story, and the story of man and mountains even in these places has only just begun. People have been present in mountain areas ever since the first hunters crept up the primordial slopes. The association of men and mountains is almost as old as that of men and the cradling sea.

THE terms of life are different in the mountains, and usually harder for man. Basically, they are set by three controlling influences and the ways in which these combine. The ruling factors are: the terrain of the mountains, the climate and the isolation from the rest of mankind that mountain living enforces.

Of these, terrain is most important. Even in the most favored climates, the mountains put forward constraints that weigh upon life. These may be overcome, but the price is high. The tilt of the land makes everything more laborious. Extra energy must be expended not only to drag burdens uphill but also to brake their descent. Every hillside field requires more work. The slope, moreover, is not simply a passive foe. It drags the very earth of man's fields downhill.

In many places round the world, men try to fight the slope with retaining walls and terraces. But terraced fields take a big effort to build and unremitting work to maintain. In the Philippines, in India and Nepal, in the densely settled valleys of southeast Asia, above all in the collectivized countryside of China, millions of people struggle throughout their lives to keep these layered fields in place. Even along the relatively gentle "Golden Slope" of the Burgundy wine country in France, the vinegrower rushes out after a rain to put back the washed-out soil with his bare hands.

The slope of the terrain, then, is a force so unfriendly that the only man on the mountain who seems to profit from it is the skier. The influence of the climate, the second fundamental factor, is somewhat more complex. In the Temperate Zones, mountain weather discourages man from making a living, blanketing the fields in white for much of the year, shortening the growing season to a bare two or three months. In the highest places of the world's temperate belt, it is simply too cold for man to live permanently. Yet in the tropics, mountains may be man's best habitat. They are free from malaria, sleeping sickness and other hot-country diseases; they have the milder temperatures and more equitable rainfall; they may even have the better soil.

The valley of Mexico, an "intermontane basin" 7,500 feet up in the continental backbone and site of the country's capital, has been a center of political power through 3,000 years of Middle American civilization. Scholars believe that the domestication of corn, which gave rise to the first civilization of the New World, probably was achieved somewhere in the highlands of Guatemala or southeastern Mexico. Bogotá in the Colombian Andes is situated almost directly on the equator, yet its altitude of 8,659 feet gives it such a cool climate that Spanish settlers have been able to preserve their customs faithfully, even to wearing black suits to their offices; it gets chilly in Bogotá just as in the Madrid they came from.

In many upland spots near the equator, there are no such changes of season as most of us are used to. In certain regions of the Bolivian and

Peruvian Andes the climate is eternal springtime, peach trees bloom all year long and fields yield several crops annually. In fact, the environment in these areas is agreeable enough to have fostered the development of the continent's only great native civilization, that of the Incas. In the course of Andean civilization's 4,000-year development, millions of people occupied the high valleys of the central Andes, and many of them established themselves long ago in some of the highest permanent habitations on earth. At extreme heights, however, the advantages of high-altitude equatorial living vanish; the air gets too thin and cold to be called friendly. For the ordinary run of mankind, in fact, the climate in the high Andes is so unfavorable that it poses what seems to be an almost unsolvable problem in survival: how does one get enough air up there to breathe?

Most of us live near the very bottom of a 10-mile-deep ocean of air. This air, having weight and being compressible, becomes denser as it gets deeper. At sea level a man is adapted to this density, or "pressure," which is 15 pounds per square inch, and his lungs are so constructed that when he breathes in a gulp of air the 15-pound pressure will force a sufficient supply of oxygen through the thin linings of his lungs to give his blood what it needs. But as one goes higher the pressure is reduced. At 10,000 feet it is down to only 10 pounds, which is not quite enough to push an adequate supply of oxygen through the linings of the lungs. As a result the blood may carry as much as 15 per cent less than its normal load of oxygen, and the lack may cause headaches, fatigue and shortness of breath. At 18,000 feet the air pressure is only half what it is at sea level, and few people will escape more pronounced symptoms. Unless the human body somehow can overcome the shortage and keep its vital oxygen balance, it will sicken and die.

Yet in the high Andes and in Tibet people not only survive at such heights but live their whole lives there, working and playing as normally as the rest of us do at sea level. Clearly these people have made tremendous use of what their communities have learned over the centuries about adjusting their daily activities to an extreme environment. But more important, they have overcome the altitude problem permanently by a dramatic adaptation. They have become physically different from the rest of us, mainly by changes in their respiratory and blood-circulating systems.

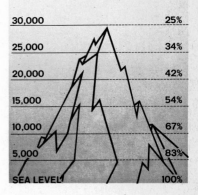

ALVEOLAR PRESSURE provides a way of measuring the amount of oxygen that can enter the blood stream at various altitudes. The term comes from the small air sacs, or alveoli, in the lungs, through whose thin membranes oxygen penetrates to the blood. This diagram, in which the "normal" alveolar pressure at sea level is figured at 100 per cent, shows how pressure decreases as the air thins out with altitude. At 30,000 feet it is only one quarter as strong as "normal."

ONE of the first things a visitor to the high Andes notices is that the stocky inhabitants of these mountain slopes have tremendous, barrel-shaped chests. And they have lungs to match. Furthermore the small pockets, or alveoli, which line the lungs and give added lung capacity are, in these people, always opened wide. This lets the greatest possible amount of blood flow through the delicate lung tissues and thus pick up all possible oxygen that is breathed in.

The Indian of the high Andes has about 20 per cent more blood than a lowlander. This extra blood is made up largely of red corpuscles, because it is red corpuscles that hold the all-important hemoglobin which catches and absorbs oxygen. In Indians living at 15,000 feet, there is an increase of almost 60 per cent by weight of this vital hemoglobin. Each of their red blood cells, moreover, is larger than the cells of lowland people, this larger size giving a greater surface for the absorption of oxygen.

Because the mountain Indian's blood is so rich in red cells, it is thicker and more viscous than that of lowlanders. And since the Andean's heart must pump harder at these heights, it is about a fifth larger. Its beat is also slower. The Andean's body is squat and compact, which means that the blood does not have to be pumped so far each time it circulates. At the end of his broad, stubby extremities are an unusually large number of direct passages between small arteries and small veins. This quickens circulation, and enables the Andean Indian to go about unconcernedly with hands and feet uncovered at times when lowlanders would suffer severe frostbite if they tried it. Like birds, these people can walk barefoot in the snow without discomfort.

The Indians of the high Andes are the relic of a civilization that carried the love of mountains far beyond that of the Scots, the Swiss or other European highlanders. This was the civilization of the Incas, which in turn was established upon the cultural foundations of an earlier people, developed over thousands of years. The Incas were great builders and organizers. Led by an emperor who was also chief priest and supreme military commander, they erected cities on the upper ridges of the snowy Andes, and imperishable stone fortresses, like storied Machu Picchu, which was rediscovered only in 1911. They built stone-surfaced highways 3,250 miles long, piped irrigation water through mountain tunnels, farmed terraced slopes at angles of 60 degrees. They colonized the mountain heights with herdsmen to tend their enormous llama herds.

When the Spanish conquered Peru in 1532, they exterminated the Inca ruling class and peonized everyone else. Today the Andean Indian is impoverished and weakened by diseases resulting from poor sanitation and chronic malnutrition. But 5.5 million of these people still speak the Quechua language of the Incas, and the basic high-country agriculture of the ancients survives.

Llamas and alpacas, mountain animals related to camels, still provide these people with the warm clothing needed at such heights. For fuel so far above the tree line, the Indians burn llama dung. The principal food of the high Andes is the potato, which was first domesticated on these slopes. Some local varieties of potato are so hardy that they keep right on growing when their leaves are white with frost.

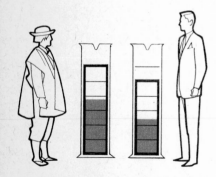

DIFFERENCES IN BLOOD between an Andean mountaineer and a sea-level dweller are shown above. Both men weigh 130 pounds, although the Andean (left) is shorter and stockier. His total blood content (shown by the heavy black line in the beaker) is six quarts, more than half of which consists of red cells. The lowlander has only five quarts, of which red cells make up less than half.

Corn grows at heights up to 12,500 feet, but it takes nine to 10 months to mature. In addition the Indians grow all sorts of odd tubers unknown at lower altitudes. They cultivate an edible mountain nasturtium. They make porridge from the seeds of a plant called Quinoa. Still they do not get enough to eat. Required to turn over half their meager produce to their landlords, they cannot afford to slaughter a llama for meat. Some try to keep guinea pigs as lowland farmers keep chickens. Lack of fat in the diet causes many people to suffer from cracks in their calloused soles, in their lips and around their eyes. Nevertheless, few leave; and of those who go to the lowlands many fall ill, frequently with tuberculosis. To dull the pain of hunger and cold, the mountain people chew the narcotic leaf of the coca plant that grows on their high slopes. In Inca times coca was reserved for the ceremonial use of priests and nobles; now nine of every 10 Andean Indians use it. As they chew and swallow their nerves are dulled; they feel warmer and stronger and imagine they are working very well.

The Andean Indians belong to the Mongoloid branch of the human race. The only other people of the world who have demonstrated the same remarkable capacity to adapt to high-altitude climate are the people of the high Himalayas, and they too are of Mongoloid origin. The Mongoloids are a group who emerged during one of the last ice ages, in northeast Asia some 360,000 years ago and, in the process of trying to survive amidst high winds and bitter cold, achieved a particularly high degree of cold-resistance. Their very bodies tend to be short and well-rounded, with short extremities that present the least possible surface area for heat loss in proportion to their size. Their noses and foreheads are flattish, their cheeks broad and fat-padded. And from above their eyes, hanging like a storm window before the upper lid when the eye is open, grows an epicanthic fold of fat that helps keep the eye from freezing.

All this made an ideal mask to protect eyes, nose and sinuses against the ice-age weather of the past. As the ice age gave ground, some Mongoloids migrated north and east across the Bering Strait land bridge to become the ancestors of the Andean and other American Indians. Others spread south to the Himalayan snows.

Whether in the Himalayas or the Andes, the Mongoloid peoples obviously have adapted well to mountain living, and this goes far in explaining why they live there now. But it does not explain why they should have settled there in the first place. For an answer to this question we must turn to the third of the basic influences that have shaped man's life in the mountains—the isolation that goes with mountain living.

IT seems evident that early man never took to the higher mountains except as he was driven by necessity, by hunger or by fear. The mountains, viewed from afar, must have seemed the land of impassable terrors, the country of wolves, cold, famine, demons. Yet these very terrors of terrain and climate tend to isolate the mountains from the plains and create there a kind of geographic sanctuary. Tibet is what anthropologists call a refuge. That is to say, it is likely that the ancestors of the present Tibetans went there ages ago not so much because they liked the place but because they hoped to gain a security in the remoteness of its mountain fastnesses that they had not been able to win elsewhere.

This they did. Tibet is a huge, inhospitable plateau about one sixth the size of the continental United States, ringed with high mountains. Its average height is 15,000 feet, and Gartok, 15,200 feet high in the northern part of the country, is credited with being the world's highest center of habitation. Not content with such a protective ring of barriers, Tibetans have guarded their isolation by every conceivable human means until their capital of Lhasa (altitude 11,830 feet) became known as "the forbidden city." They tried to bar all people from the outside world—and until the seizure of Tibet by Communist China in 1951, succeeded fairly well. They resisted new ideas and new ways. And in what seems to be a trait of high-altitude societies (the Andes produced the Incas, the Arabian mountain state of Yemen is still ruled by an Imam), they built up a theocracy. Tibet's was a kind of Buddhist state in which every third male was a monk and the Dalai Lama, or god-king, was supreme over all things spiritual and temporal. Even their theology was shaped by the mountain climate: the hell of Tibetan Buddhism is a cold place.

The key to life for the people of the high Tibetan plateau is that shaggy, ill-tempered relative of the buffalo called the yak. As an all-purpose, high-altitude friend to man, the yak beats even the llama. One does not milk a llama. But the yak furnishes meat, wool, milk, butter and transport. Tibetan peasants spend their lives at the lonely task of herding yaks from one thin pasture to the next. For a year at a time they may be away from any village, living in portable tents made of yak hair and kept warm by fires fueled with yak dung. As in the Andes, the few who stay in the valleys and work the fields labor mostly for others. Their scant fields yield barley, some peas and wheat, and occasionally potatoes. The people live in solid huts made of sun-dried bricks, flat, earthen roofs and support-timbers laboriously dragged up the mountainsides from Nepalese or Chinese forests. Since Tibetan men are so often away for long spells herding yaks, several often share a single wife. On the other hand, the women enjoy similar freedom. They may, and often do, take several husbands. In fact, when she marries a man a Tibetan girl may also marry his brothers.

For such devoutly faithful Buddhists, who normally have religious scruples about eating meat, the mountain people of high Tibet and the Himalayas follow a strange diet. As far as they can afford it, they eat meat—yak meat. The butter made from yak milk is also of first importance. They pay their rent and taxes in yak butter. They make their pious presents to lamas and monks in butter. At high festivals they even parade statues of sculpt butter. And the national drink is buttered tea—tea laced with rancid yak butter. People drink 30 to 50 cups of it daily and worry about their well-being if they get less. Visitors find this brew unbearably greasy but it adds fat to the Tibetan's diet and fortifies him against the Himalayan blasts. Though Tibetans also eat a lot of parched barley, they are not intensive cultivators of the land, like the Andean Indians. They are a pastoral people. In all, 1.5 million of them occupy an area many times greater than the central Andean uplands in which four times that many Peruvian and Bolivian Indians must grow their crops and tend their flocks.

The Tibetans and other peoples of the high Himalayas are not the only ones to have found advantage in the refuge that mountains afford. Defeated people everywhere have fled before the conquerors of their rich plains and settled in fastnesses where no one would challenge their right to land that is so little favored and so hard to get at. The Atlas Mountains of North Africa are a sanctuary for the Berber tribes who sought shelter there 12 centuries ago from invading Moslem hordes. In the Mediterranean basin, which seems to have experienced a gradual drying-up at the end of the last glacial period, the mountain valleys around the rain-catching peaks may also have been a refuge for man against the natural invader of the lowlands—drought. Lebanon, a high-country Christian bastion at the eastern end of the Mediterranean, appears to be a mountain sanctuary for its people from both human and natural foes.

OVER the ages the terrors of rugged terrain and climate have tended to isolate the Alps, the Pyrenees, the Caucasus, the Apennines and other famous mountains of the European continent from the plains. There people can be relatively immune to invasion. They have no human competition. The narrow approaches to these natural fortresses are easily guarded, their highway passes well suited to ambush. Behind such ramparts, the taste of liberty flourishes—both in brigands and in burghers.

Mountains are good places for nations to get started. The Swiss mountaineers won the first local self-government in modern Europe when they formed the Swiss Confederation in the high Alps around the St. Gotthard Pass in 1291. The people of Andorra, who live in the Pyrenees between France and Spain, have guarded their own ways and the independence of their tiny republic through centuries, and still get on quite well by smuggling. That is much the story of the world's smallest republic, 1,500-year-old San Marino, perched profitably in the midst of Italy's Apennines. The people who live in the Appalachian Mountains of the southern United States preserve something archaic in their way of life, even an archaic way of speaking. They keep illicit stills, they feud, they provide the ranks of the United States Army with some of its most expert marksmen. The state motto of West Virginia is: "Mountaineers are always free men."

But they are out of touch, for though mountains keep out interlopers, they also keep the mountaineers in. Like a prisoner in his cell, the isolated mountain man is apt to hear of the innovations of mankind only in part and very late. Mountain societies are not the sort that tend to originate novelties, to agitate for change. On the contrary, they are often relics—Rip van Winkles. Until well into the 20th Century an obscure Caucasian mountain tribe called the Khevsurs still wore armor like crusader knights. There are said to be Indian tribesmen living in the remote mountains of southeastern Mexico who do not know that the country has gained its freedom from Spain, and indeed do not know that the Spaniards conquered the country in the first place.

MANY-PURPOSE ANIMAL, the yak supports human life in the uplands of Tibet. A tamed, native ox, it can be saddled, as shown above. It supplies milk, hair for clothes, hide for tents, dung for fuel, and is the Tibetans' principal source of meat.

From all this we can see that the isolation that mountains enforce upon those who live in them is as powerful as either of the other two big factors of mountain geography, terrain and climate. We may sum up these influences in one word: environment. Yet when we see how man in the mountains has matched himself against a thousand different combinations of these three variables, it seems plain that man's own resourceful nature is just as big a part of the mountain story. Man is the most adaptable animal on earth. This capacity to adapt himself enables him to go almost anywhere he wants, and adds the baffling dimension of human motivation to the story of man and mountains.

This human factor is bound to raise questions rather than answer them. Is there an inner necessity as well as an external one that drives mountain dwellers to settle where they are? Why do some peoples take to the mountains in one country and not in another? Why, for instance, is there a long hostility to mountain-living among the civilized peoples of southeast Asia? Though the English have shown with their tea plantations in upland Assam that the mountains can be profitably settled and exploited, the people of this region have persistently left their mountaintops to the primitive remnants they have displaced. Conversely, why, when life in the mountain regions of Europe is more arduous than in the lowlands, do these highlanders stay rather than move down? Is it some kind of termite blindness, some absence of elementary initiative, some obstinate need for security that holds them there? For this last question at least, an answer can be hazarded: some people are not mountaineers by deliberate choice; they are far too absorbed in the problems of existing from day to day to spend much thought comparing their lot with the alternative of life on the plains.

The peopling of the mountains follows no logic, and the accidents that probably account for what happened are lost in the mists of history and prehistory. Human geography is a riddle. The scientists can measure ancient skulls and they can take similar measurements of the living. They can study the frequency with which individuals of certain blood types turn up in certain parts of the world. They can analyze the mysterious kinships of men's languages. Sometimes mountain peoples give us some clues by their being where they are now. But how, for example, are we to account for the Basques, a people who live in the Pyrenees and have preserved through long centuries a language utterly unlike that of their neighbors or any other people on earth?

THESE are questions that touch on the even more basic and more difficult one of how early man in general distributed himself about the globe. Almost nothing is known about this, one reason being that scientists are not yet sure where man originated. The rapidly growing number of primitive skulls found in recent years and the intensive study that has been devoted to classifying them are beginning to shed some light on this fascinating question, and recent evidence begins to suggest that Africa may have been the cradle of Homo sapiens. If so, he got to Asia some time during the last million years, presumably during interglacial periods, threading his way between the Caucasus and Ural ranges. And those men who penetrated beyond the Himalayas, although they may have been trapped somewhat later behind subsequent ice sheets and developed into what we now recognize as the Mongoloid race, may have been, and probably were, the same people originally as those we now call the Caucasoid race. There may turn out to be a totally different explanation for the original distribution and subsequent differentiation of these two great races of man, but there is no question that mountains have kept them separate for a long time and helped to create the differences that now exist between them. The other two great races of man apparently were not separated by mountains. The Negroes of Africa probably have been kept where they are by the barrier of the Sahara desert to the north of them, and the aborigines of Australia by the ocean, which rose to cut their continental island off from Asia after they had wandered there.

Men do not cross mountains by choice. Pilgrims, peddlers, migrating tribes and invading armies alike tend to take the low road. The oldest known track across Europe is the Amber Trail, so-called for the one highly prized item that the Stone Age tribesmen had to exchange for the products of the more advanced Mediterranean peoples. For thousands of years men followed this track from the Baltic, where the amber could be found on the beaches, south to the gap between the Bohemian and Carpathian ranges forming the present northern frontier of Czechoslovakia, and on through Bohemia to the Danube crossing at Vienna, and so by one or another of three low Yugoslavian passes to the Mediterranean.

The so-called Carpathian Gap through which this trail passes has been fought over throughout European history. Napoleon won his decisive battle for the mastery of Europe in 1805 by defeating the combined Austrian and Russian armies at Austerlitz, close by the Bohemian part of the Amber Trail. Austria, which also lies on the Amber Trail, is what geographers call a "pass state." In addition to the ancient north-south track of the

Amber Trail, Austria is traversed from east to west by a natural highway that starts in eastern Europe, cuts through the Transylvanian Alps at the Danube's Iron Gate, and runs on past Vienna between the Alps and the Bohemian mountains into what is now southern Germany.

Such mountain gaps, or natural gateways, have played a tremendous part in the settlement of the United States, particularly the Cumberland Gap through which Carolina and Virginia families began trekking west. Through the Gap ran the famous Wilderness Road, by which Daniel Boone, John Sevier, the grandfather of Abraham Lincoln, and other pioneers moved on to settle the state of Kentucky. Similarly, the Mohawk valley was an almost water-level route to the Great Lakes between the Catskills and Adirondacks. The Erie Canal was driven through this gap, and in the dawning industrial age the railroads were pushed through. Men and goods began to move between Europe and the New West through New York City and the Mohawk gap instead of down the Mississippi and through New Orleans. No doubt, the Mohawk gateway through the mountains helped make New York first among American cities. Later Americans, pressing farther westward, found another such natural opening through the Rocky Mountains of southern Wyoming. This was the famous South Pass, through which covered wagons could roll across the continental divide whether bound for the Northwest by the Oregon Trail or for California by the Donner or Truckee Passes. The American geographer William Gilpin, regarding the South Pass as the gateway between the Atlantic and Pacific worlds, exuberantly proposed in the 1860s that it be named the Pillars of Washington, and forecast that Denver, as the city commanding its approaches, would inevitably become the pivot of creation.

Passes make history—and legend. Hannibal, Attila and Napoleon all won renown for daring marches across high Alpine passes. Possibly the most famous holding action in history was fought in 480 B.C. at the narrow defile of Thermopylae, where Leonidas and 300 Greeks held the pass until all were killed by the Persian hosts, and thus gave the Greek navy time to rally and end the invasion threat by destroying the Persian fleet.

Another great story of rear-guard gallantry is enshrined in the medieval *Chanson de Roland*. As recited by the crusaders, sung by bards to Norman warriors going into battle at Hastings in 1066 and still familiar to every Western schoolboy, this is the story of how the chivalrous nephew of Charlemagne died fighting off the infidel Moorish hordes at the pass of Roncesvalles in the rugged Pyrenees. Far from being a glorious stand against the infidel, Roncesvalles was the worst fiasco of Charlemagne's military career. Foiled in an attempt to extend his rule beyond the Pyrenees by the indifference of the Christian population of northern Spain, Charlemagne was leading his forces back over the mountains when his Frankish ranks at the rear fell victims of an ambush.

The Franks had not even bothered to scout the heights to see if the pass was clear. Under Count Hroudland of Brittany, the Franks were caught in disarray as they straggled in their bulky armor up the narrow forest trail. The mountaineers, apparently unencumbered by any armor at all, slaughtered the Franks to the last man. Too proud to call for help, Hroudland, or Roland, waited until too late to blow his horn. When he arrived, Charlemagne found nothing but looted bodies and carts. The attackers had melted into their mountains. And who were they? Not Moslems at all but fellow Christians—Basque guerrillas who struck boldly because they were sure the Franks were not coming back. They never did come back. From that day on, the Pyrenees became the southern frontier of Charlemagne's realm, and they have been a frontier ever since.

In leading his forces into a mountain ambush, Charlemagne ignored the instructive example of an earlier conqueror. When Alexander the Great marched east to extend his empire in 327 B.C., he was too cunning to advance through the Khyber Pass, the historic invasion gateway to India but also the warpath of fierce mountain fighters. Circling north among the 18,000-foot peaks of the rugged Hindu Kush, Alexander swept down on India by one of the Indus River's northerly tributaries.

A kind of natural boundary governs war between mountain and plains people. When Francisco Pizarro led his Spanish conquistadors into the Andes, he is supposed to have plotted his whole campaign to get around this physiological barrier. By a cunning trick he seized the Inca emperor for a hostage the day after his party reached the high-altitude country, then settled down at Cajamarca to get used to the height before marching to the capital of Cuzco. When Bolivia and Paraguay fought their jungle Chaco war in the 1920s, the Bolivian mountaineers were hopeless losers in the lowland swamps. They all fell sick. But when the Paraguayans tried carrying the fight up the heights, the rigors were too much for their jungle fighters. They in turn fell back.

MOUNTAINS have always filled men with a sense of the supernatural. Once men thought the peaks kept the sky from falling in. To the early Greeks the Pillars of Hercules, looming up at either side of the Strait of Gibraltar, held up that end of the universe. The ancient Chinese identified five mountains—Heng Shan in the north, Sun Chan in the center, Hua Shan in the west, Heng Shan in the south and T'ai Shan in the east—as the props of the sky. According to a legend a red-cheeked dragon named Kung Kung once rushed at the northern Heng Shan and knocked the celestial canopy askew, causing a global tilt to the southeast, and great floods.

Mountains bespeak the silence and the eloquence of nature. They make man look up, and feel the nearness of the heavens. High places are holy places. Moses received the Ten Commandments on Mount Sinai, Buddha was born in the shadow of the Himalayas. Great monasteries—the Potala in Lhasa, the hospice of Saint Bernard, the cloisters of Mount Athos—are in high places. The Golden Lotus that the Hindu creator Vishnu first caused to rise from the void had for its petals the summits of the Himalayas, and from its heart ran a river saturated with holiness, the sacred Ganges. The prophet Ezekiel placed earthly paradise on a high mountain, from which living waters flowed. The Greeks placed their pantheon on Mount Olympus, of which Homer sang: "Shaken by no wind, drenched by no showers, and invaded by no snows, it is set in a cloudless sea of limpid air with a white radiance playing over all. There the happy gods spend their delightful days...."

Within the past decade man himself has walked on the highest mountaintops. But the heights still fill him with awe and the sense of mystery. The words of the Psalmist continue to echo in the hearts of men: "I will lift up mine eyes unto the hills whence cometh my help."

A STONE CROSS MEMORIALIZES THE VICTIMS OF A LANDSLIDE IN THE ANDES AND ACTS AS A TALISMAN AGAINST FUTURE DISASTER

Of Mountain Men

Living higher above sea level than anyone else on earth, the peoples of the Himalayas and the Andes have become uniquely adapted to high altitude. Their bodies can withstand extreme cold and severe shortages of oxygen, and they have a great capacity for hard work. The challenges presented by mountain life have also encouraged in them strong religious feelings.

Andean Peoples

The Andean Indian is a kind of underprivileged superman. Though poorly fed and badly overworked, he has evolved into one of the physical marvels of the world, having become uniquely adapted to the harsh conditions of high-altitude life. On the 13,000-foot Altiplano tableland the air pressure is about eight pounds per square inch compared to 15 pounds at sea level, and the temperature drops below freezing almost daily throughout much of the year. To meet the problem of thin air the Indian has acquired a set of oversized lungs in an oversized chest, and his blood and tissues make extremely efficient use of oxygen. To resist cold, generations of adaptive

NIMBLE-FINGERED BOLIVIAN, wearing a jaunty derby, unravels guanaco wool before threading it onto a free-swinging spindle. The hand-held device enables her to spin at odd moments of the day between caring for the baby on her back and preparing *chuño*.

PREPARING CHUNO, a dried potato mash that is the chief food of the Andean Indian, women remove the skins from thousands of marble-sized tubers (*right*). The potatoes are then trampled and dried. Keeping indefinitely, *chuño* is the basis of many dishes.

mutations have given the Indian stumpy arms and legs and a short torso, so that his blood has a shorter distance in which to circulate. With many capillaries to warm his extremities, he can walk barefoot in snow without ill effect.

But in spite of his physical adaptation to the heights the Indian has a hard time of it there. Though his Incan ancestors once ruled the Altiplano, he is now pathetically exploited. As a tenant farmer he works only for permission to grow crops of his own. His diet is invariable: beans, potatoes, quinoa and, rarely, a little mutton. Dysentery and whooping cough take many of his children, and he himself does not live long.

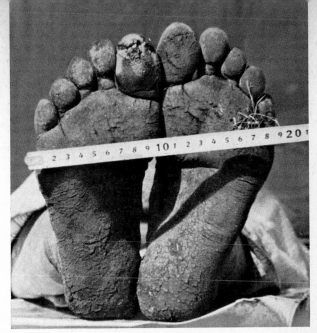

GNARLED FEET of a mountain man are wide, and so well supplied with blood vessels that they are almost immune to cold. This man was found walking barefoot in the snow.

GIGANTIC LOADS of potatoes bend the backs of Indian farm hands 11,000 feet up in the Peruvian Andes. Badly exploited, these men begin work as boys paid 60 cents a day. As they mature and can carry heavier loads, they are paid more, sometimes on a piecework basis, but rarely does the per capita income of the Indian exceed $65 a year.

A Life of Toil and Coca

The dazed, half-dreaming face peering upward on the opposite page belongs to an Andean Indian under the influence of the narcotic cocaine. Like millions of his race, both men and women, he has become addicted to it by constant daily chewing of the leaves of the coca plant.

The prevalence of the habit presents a thorny problem for South American governments. Peru has tried to restrict coca production to limit its use but has had very little success. The Indian does not want to give it up. Born to a life of unremitting hunger and backbreaking toil, he chews to numb his senses. It greatly reduces his working efficiency, but without it he becomes depressed and unwilling to work at all. Although addiction probably shortens his life (most Indians do not live beyond the age of 40), coca is so important to him that he has made it an object of veneration, believing that coca was divinely given to him through his ancestors, the Incas.

HARVESTING COCA, women pick leaves from plants on a terraced Bolivian farm. As payment the landlord gives the workers land to grow their own coca and a few basic crops.

LEAD MINER, befuddled by coca-chewing (*opposite*), stumbles out of a Peruvian lead mine with a heavy load of ore. One day's wage for this worker averages about $1.25.

143

NEATLY FITTED INCA WALL OF STONE, STILL IN PERFECT CONDITION, IS INCORPORATED INTO A MODERN BUILDING IN CUZCO, PERU

STURDY RUIN of an Inca town stands forgotten in the mountains of Peru. Though plain and sparsely furnished, these were the homes of high Inca government officials.

A Lost Empire in the High Andes

Only rarely have mountain peoples been conquerors. Mountain terrain makes military campaigning difficult; in addition, the more basic struggle to exist at all on the heights uses up surplus energies. The Incas were an exception: in the 13th Century they consolidated an Andean empire reaching from Ecuador to Argentina.

The secret of their success was a ruthless socialism resembling modern communism. Headed by an earthly deity, the Inca, the state owned all property, each man's needs being provided for by a vast bureaucracy. Using slave labor, they built mountaintop cities of beautifully fitted stone (*left*) and hundreds of miles of paved roads and farming terraces (*opposite*). When the Incas themselves fell in 1532, it was to a conqueror as ruthless as they: the Spaniard Pizarro.

MOUNTAIN STAIRWAY of farming terraces (*opposite*), built by the Incas, clings to an Andean peak. Indians today continue to use them as the Incas did, for growing potatoes.

HUGE CATCH of silver-blue fish is spread out to dry by Peru's Lake Titicaca. After locating a school of fish, the Indians beat the water behind it and drive it into nets.

ANCIENT REED BOATS, called "little horses," date from pre-Inca times. An all-purpose material, reeds are used to make roofs, doors, beds and even houses.

GRINDING CORN, an Indian boy uses a Stone Age method (*right*). He rolls a flat-sided stone over the kernels, crushing them to powder on his rock table.

Himalayan Peoples

Work is hard and riches are few in the Himalayas, but life is better there for the average inhabitant than in the Andes. Neither the Tibetan nomad herder nor the Nepalese terrace farmer wants for basic necessities like food and clothing. In Tibet most of these are provided by the amazing yak, an all-in-one source of wool, leather, meat, milk, cheese, transport, and dung for fuel and fertilizer. It is not uncommon for a man to own a herd of 200 or more yaks.

On the steep slopes south of the Himalayas, herding is impractical, so the natives are predominantly farmers. A heavy rainfall helps compensate for poor soil and every foot of ground is tilled, the crops varying with altitude. In the warmer, relatively lush lowlands (*opposite*), as many as three crops a year of staples like rice and corn can be harvested. In the colder uplands (*below*), potatoes and wheat are grown.

FILLING HER COOKING BOWLS, a Nepalese woman taps a leather water bag. Usually made from yak or buffalo skins, these bags are also used for chang, the local barley beer.

ENDLESS TERRACES scallop a steep valley in Nepal (*opposite*). Farmed by hand—the plow is almost unknown—these narrow ledges make up most of Nepal's arable land.

DIGGING POTATOES, Sherpa women wield crude hoes in the highlands of Nepal. A Sherpa staple introduced by the British in 1850, potatoes do well in the cold, wet climate.

WINSOME MOUNTAIN GIRL from a Moslem tribe in Baltistan, Kashmir, flings away her veil in an unusual demonstration of boldness. Ordinarily the women of this small province hide their faces when approached by foreigners. Unlike the women of neighboring Tibet, who often have several husbands, Kashmir women are still treated as serfs.

ARCHAIC ARMY of Bhutan, a tiny Himalayan kingdom between India and Tibet, marches in 15th Century armor to a coronation in 1952. These troops may carry rifles, but bows and arrows are still widely used. Though technically backward, Bhutan is up-to-date in other ways. Slavery has been abolished and women have been granted equal rights.

THE 1,000-ROOM "POTALA" IN LHASA, CAPITAL OF TIBET, WAS THE PALACE OF THE DALAI LAMA BEFORE RED CHINA'S TAKE-OVER

Many Faiths of Mountain Peoples

The intense preoccupation of mountain people with religion is nowhere more marked than in the Himalayas. Before its take-over by Red China, Lamaist Tibet was traditionally run by a religious ruler, the Dalai Lama. With one out of every three men spending at least part of his life as a monk, the country was filled with monasteries, some with as many as 7,000 members. Besides revering Buddha, Tibetans also propitiate a host of evil spirits which they believe infest the air around them.

In Nepal, Hinduism and Buddhism thrive together and many people embrace both faiths. This has given rise to an incredibly intricate and amalgamated religion curiously tolerant of all gods yet rigorous in its demands on its followers.

GODDESS OF SACRIFICE, the Hindu deity Kali (*opposite*), leers over Katmandu, Nepal. Every year the Nepalese propitiate Kali by smearing her grim idol with goat blood.

A STERN-FACED LAMA wears the robes of a high priest of Lamaism in Bhutan (*below*). Like many Himalayans, he has a large goiter long thought to be caused by iodine deficiency.

Holy Men of Lamaism

Living in the loftiest land in the world, the Tibetans are, fittingly, the most deeply concerned of any mountain people with things of the spirit. The highest calling in Tibet is that of the monk and lama. A long ladder of preferment, however, faces the novice in a religious career. At the top stands the Dalai Lama, a god incarnate who is chief of Tibetan Lamaism although the country is in the hands of Red China and he himself is in exile.

At the bottom is the lowly monk for whom comparable status can only come after a 50-year preparation in monasteries. This consists of intense study of Buddhist and Tibetan scripture, and training in debate. Daylong classes are interrupted only for psalm-chanting and tea-drinking. Ultimately a fortunate monk may rise from student to teacher to abbot and one day to Gan-Dan Khri-Pa. Then he too will be a living god.

TWO LIVING GODS, pillars of Tibetan Lamaism, are the Dalai Lama (*left*) and the Panchen Lama. Today the former is in exile, the latter is a Red puppet ruler.

A MEETING OF MONKS gathers in a monastery in pre-Communist Tibet (*right*). To discredit Lamaism the Red Chinese forced many monasteries to disband.

7

The Lure
of the Peaks

AMONG all the great events of the year 1492 there is one remembered chiefly by those for whom mountain climbing is a passion. In that historic year, Antoine de Ville, Chamberlain to King Charles VIII of France, obeyed his majesty's royal command by leading a party of climbers to the top of Mont Aiguille. This peak in the Dauphiné Alps near Grenoble had a reputation of being an "inaccessible mountain." De Ville courageously proved otherwise. He even spent three days on its summit before coming down to write his "first, full, precise, and detailed account" of the first recorded attempt by man to climb a substantial mountain simply to get to the top.

The first real outbreak of mountain climbing enthusiasm occurred before the middle of the 16th Century and included no less a personage than Leonardo da Vinci, who clambered up the southern slopes of the Pennines. The movement was concentrated in Zurich and its leader was Conrad Gesner, an eminent naturalist who was resolved, for his "mental delight," to climb at least one peak every year. This enthusiasm died out, however, and apparently the next mountain climbing expedition did not take place until midway in the next century, in America. The climber was Darby Field of Exeter, New Hampshire, who climbed Mount Washington, the highest peak in the Presidential Range, in June 1642. Only two of Field's Indian guides were willing to defy superstition by accompanying him to the summit. The Indians believed that the mountain was the abode of the Great Spirit, who would surely strike dead anyone daring to invade its upper slopes. Field not only climbed and survived but was so impressed by the view from the top that he returned about a month later for a second ascent. This time he brought along five or six other pioneers.

Today, neither Mont Aiguille (6,880 feet) nor Mount Washington (6,288 feet) seems much of a challenge. Even the summit of Mont Blanc (15,781 feet)—highest in the Alps—has become a vantage point enjoyed by many a tourist. Yet, as recently as 200 years ago no one was willing to risk his life by making the first ascent of Mont Blanc to win a prize offered in 1760 by the famous Swiss naturalist, Horace Bénédict de Saussure. The prize went begging for 26 years. Then a crystal hunter, Jacques Balmat, and the physician Michel G. Paccard of Chamonix finally made the climb and claimed the reward. The following year, De Saussure himself repeated the feat, taking his valet and 18 guides headed by Balmat with him. Mountaineers regard De Saussure as the first real patron of modern climbing.

Still, for a long while few people seemed to think of climbing for the joy of reaching the top. Even those who lived among the mountains did not climb them. Indeed, mountains were considered by many to be excrescences of Nature, horrible faults in the Divine Plan. Eighteenth Century travelers crossing the Alps sometimes requested blindfolds—not to avoid vertigo but because their sense of harmony was offended by the sight of such wild irregularities in the earth's surface. An old Chinese proverb reflects the prevailing attitude: "There are many paths to the top of the mountain, but the view is always the same."

THE spark of adventure glowed more brightly in 1854, when a Britisher on his honeymoon, Sir Alfred Wills, pitted himself against the particularly difficult Wetterhorn (12,166 feet). Other Englishmen accepted similar challenges, and the golden age of mountaineering had begun. During the next 16 years, Britons climbed every one of the principal summits in Europe, communicating, as they did so, their enthusiasm to their Swiss, French or Italian guides. Some hidden quirk of Anglo-Saxon temperament seems to have been waiting for the call of high mountains. British climbers are largely responsible for the development of mountaineering.

Probably the most famous, tragic and long-debated climb of these early years was Edward Whymper's ascent in 1865 of the Matterhorn (14,685 feet) in the Pennine Alps between Switzerland and Italy. The Matterhorn was then supposed to be invincible. It is one of the most beautiful and dramatic peaks in the world, standing like a spike against the sky above the Swiss village of Zermatt, its sides appearing nearly vertical when viewed from the valley below.

Whymper, when he made his famous ascent, was only 26 years old. He was, however, versed in the Alps. Sent to Switzerland in 1860 by a London publisher to make sketches, he had become fascinated with the mountains and with climbing, had returned every summer and had made a number of considerable ascents. He had tried the Matterhorn seven times but, like many others, had failed. On one occasion (1863) he had been pinned down on the mountain's upper slopes by a ferocious storm which lasted 26 hours.

After this reverse it occurred to Whymper that he and other climbers had been attempting the mountain from the wrong side, the Italian side. This was because from the Swiss side, looking up from Zermatt, the climb appeared impossible (to a nonclimber it still does). But Whymper discovered that what looks like a near-perpendicular slope reveals itself, when seen from a different angle, to be only a 40-degree grade. He also reasoned, from observing how the snow clung to the Matterhorn's upper flank, that what appeared to be an utterly smooth rock face was in actuality a series of terraces.

WHYMPER'S ROUTE up the Matterhorn's flanks to its 14,685-foot peak is indicated by the solid line at right. "X" indicates where four of the seven climbers in this 1865 expedition fell to their deaths. The dotted line shows the route of descent.

So Whymper decided in 1865 to try from the Swiss side. But he was stalled because he could not persuade his favorite guide, Carrel, an Italian, to go with him. Then one evening he met a 19-year-old Englishman, Lord Francis Douglas, a practiced climber, and they decided to join forces. In Zermatt they found Peter Taugwalder, a veteran guide, who agreed to come and bring along his son, "young Peter." As Whymper and Douglas were discussing their plans in a Zermatt hotel, in walked the Reverend Charles Hudson, perhaps the ablest English mountaineer of the day. He had two companions with him, a young man named Douglas Hadow, and the greatest guide from Chamonix, Michel-Auguste Croz. Hudson was also planning to try the Matterhorn. In a few moments the two parties had agreed to join forces. The charming informality of these arrangements was to prove a fatal mistake. Hadow had evidently represented himself to Hudson as an experienced climber, and Whymper took Hudson's word for it. Actually Hadow had only made two ascents in his life and had proved a bungler both times.

On the next fine day the expedition set out for the Matterhorn. The first part of the ascent was so easy that by noon the climbers reached the spot where they intended to camp. There, at 11,000 feet, they set up a tent and Croz and young Peter went on above to reconnoiter. These scouts returned at three o'clock with the glad news that the rest of the climb looked astonishingly easy. That night the party gaily talked and sang until well after dark.

The following morning they were on the move early and reached 14,000 feet by 9:55. There were less than 1,000 feet to go. Despite the fact that Hadow required constant assistance, the party reached the top by 1:40 p.m., Whymper and Croz running up the last 200 feet. An hour later they began the descent, roped together for safety and with Hadow between the sure-footed Croz and the almost equally capable Hudson. Douglas was next on the rope, then the elder Taugwalder, Whymper and young Peter. All would have been well but for Hadow, who was so helpless that Croz actually had to turn around every few steps and place Hadow's feet, one by one, in their proper positions.

It was at such a moment that the tragedy occurred. As Croz turned around, Hadow lost his footing and fell against the guide. Croz, taken by surprise and unable to bear the weight, fell backward with a cry. The rope pulled Hudson and then Douglas off balance. Whymper and the two Taugwalders, alerted by the cry, grabbed frantically at the nearest rocks. They felt a terrific jerk but held. Then, suddenly, they felt nothing. The rope had broken. As Whymper wrote later: "For a few seconds we saw our unfortunate companions sliding downwards on their backs, and spreading out their hands, endeavoring to save themselves. They passed from our sight uninjured, disappeared one by one, and fell from precipice to precipice on to the Matterhorn Glacier below, a distance of nearly 4000 feet. So perished our comrades!"

Whymper later discovered not only the fact of Hadow's inexperience but also that the rope they had been using was their third best, old and unreliable, which they had brought along only in case of an emergency. So, through ineptitude, faulty organization, faulty equipment, four men were lost. The tragedy was still a live issue in Chamonix well into this century, for Croz's fellow townsmen remained convinced that their great guide could never have fallen unless there had been some kind of treachery. They insisted that Whymper or one of the Swiss guides had cut the rope to save himself. No evidence of this was ever brought forward, however, and the story slowly died. Since then at least 100,000 people have climbed the Matterhorn, including a 76-year-old man and an 11-year-old girl who made the ascent on the same day. However, during this same period the mountain has claimed more than 90 lives, among them four cocky young men who boasted in 1948 that they could get a cow to the summit, but were later found frozen to death.

AFTER 1870, mountaineers began attacking the same summits by more hazardous routes, and also looking around for spectacular mountains in other parts of the world. As higher and more difficult peaks were attempted, the need for teamwork increased. No longer did most climbers operate alone or with a friend or two as Whymper had on most of his climbs. Instead a party had to inch its collective way upward, tied together by a sturdy rope. Special equipment also became necessary for steep and slippery places. The old-style iron-tipped pole (alpenstock) was replaced by a strong, lightweight ice ax with which to hack steps in steep snow slopes or to use as an anchor to hold the climbing rope when footholds were few or treacherous. It doubled, too, as a hammer with which to drive iron pegs into rock crevices or solid ice. To these pegs (pitons) a ring could be fastened and through it a rope might be tied or let slip as wanted for climbing a vertical rock wall. For better footing on ice and hard snow slopes, ice graspers (crampons) were devised, sharp steel spikes that can be strapped to the soles of a climber's boots.

Around the turn of the century, one famous peak after another surrendered to the determined mountaineers. An expedition led by Edward A. Fitzgerald in 1897 reached the summit of Aconcagua (22,834 feet) in the Andes of Argentina—the highest point in the Western Hemisphere. Shortly thereafter the British explorer Sir Halford Mackinder hired two Alpine guides to assist him in tackling Mount Kenya (17,040 feet) in East Africa, a magnificent isolated old volcano rising to a massive jagged tower.

A far more elaborate expedition was needed to conquer the Mountains of the Moon—the Ruwenzori range—along the boundary between Uganda and the Congo. These mountains are extraordinarily difficult to climb since they are protected near their summits by "Ruwenzori weather"—almost perpetual mists and rain and snow—and at their bases by thick jungle and spongy undergrowth. The first successful ascent of these peaks was organized carefully in 1906 by the Italian admiral and explorer, the Duke of Abruzzi, who led an expedition of more than 300 porters, six scientists, four Alpine guides, the great Alpine photographer Vittorio Sella, and a competent cook. The duke proceeded to map the range in detail and climbed both of the highest summits—Margherita (16,821 feet) and Alexandra (16,750 feet).

THE greatest tests of man's ability to reach high places were the hardest to approach. Tibet and Nepal, in which the bulk of the Himalaya chain rises skyward, had traditional policies of excluding Europeans. The first explorers of this highest of the world's mountain ranges were Englishmen and Indians employed by the British Trigonometrical Survey. By disguising themselves as Nepalese herdsmen, Buddhist pilgrims and Tibetan merchants, a number of adventurers did penetrate the frontiers of these forbidden lands. Many disappeared; a few returned with surreptitious photographs and measurements; still fewer traveled beyond the more civilized towns to reach tiny communities in the high foothills where herdsmen were willing to aid them in climbing the lower peaks. The ascent of Mount Kabru (24,002 feet) was claimed in 1883 by W. W. Graham. It remained the highest summit reached for almost 50 years.

The Tibetan gateway to the Himalayas was opened slightly in the spring of 1904, when a military mission from British India was dispatched to put an end to friction and armed raids along the Tibetan border. Sir Francis Younghusband, who led this expeditionary force, penetrated all the way to the capital city of Lhasa and extracted a number of concessions from the Dalai Lama and his government. Most of these agreements concerned the border. But among them, possibly because Sir Francis was an ardent mountaineer, was permission for an occasional British expedition to enter Tibet for the purpose of exploring the Himalayas.

This barrier overcome, the mountains themselves proved to have extraordinary barriers of their own. First of all, there were the steep Himalayan glaciers, approachable only by way of chaotic jumbles of broken blocks called icefalls. Over these, progress was painfully slow. Once on a glacier, each party had to beware of treacherous crevasses and dodge almost daily avalanches. Worst of all, climbers still had to brave ferocious gales and snowstorms which threatened to sweep them and their equipment off the ridges—and sometimes did.

But the greatest difficulty for men coming to the Himalayas after living close to sea level was and is the inadequacy of oxygen. Oxygen constitutes 21 per cent of air, and as the air gets thinner with altitude, the available oxygen is correspondingly decreased. This has a severe effect on the sea-level dweller, although he can, in time, become as used to operating at altitudes in excess of 14,000 feet as that stand-by of Himalayan climbing expeditions, the Sherpa porter. But even the Sherpa faces problems above 18,000 feet. His mental processes are dulled, he becomes slow in decision and action, his vision weakens. Even the simplest exertion requires great mental effort and takes a terrible physical toll. He can climb for only half a dozen steps before being forced to stop—only to breathe. His heart races and his blood becomes thick and sluggish, increasing the peril of frostbite at high-altitude temperatures. Above 25,000 feet, many climbers have had vivid hallucinations, carrying on conversations with an imaginary companion

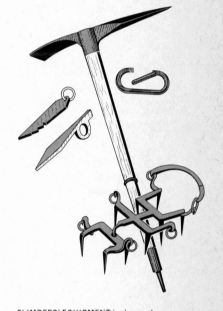

CLIMBERS' EQUIPMENT is shown above. The ice ax, second only to rope as an essential of mountaineering, is designed to probe dubious snow and rock as well as to cut steps in icy slopes. Crampons, at bottom, for work in snow and ice, fit over shoes and act much like football cleats.

Spikes, or pitons, at left, are driven into cracks to make toe and fingerholds, the toothed spike being used in ice. The snap ring, or carabiner, at right, clips on a piton ring for working with rope.

on a rope. All the high-altitude mountaineer can think of is to get down, get the job over and go home. As the great George Leigh-Mallory said. he is "like a sick man walking in a dream."

Nevertheless, climbers both before and after World War I reached the summits of a number of Himalayan peaks. Graham's record was broken in 1930 with the successful ascent of Jonsong Peak (24,340 feet), a great snow mountain north of Kanchenjunga, by members of an international party organized in Switzerland. Of course, the men who attempted Everest in the 1920s and got near its summit had climbed higher than anyone else, but they had not topped their mountain. In 1931 the record was broken once more by an English party which reached the top of Kamet (25,447 feet), about midway between the two ends of the Himalayan chain. Then came Nanda Devi (25,660 feet), the highest peak climbed up to 1950.

AFTER the war, mountaineers began to benefit from research aimed at increasing the efficiency and safety of high-altitude flight. "Walk-about" bottles of compressed oxygen were made lighter. Special face masks and regulator valves were developed, reducing the chance that the oxygen supply would fail at a critical altitude. With these improvements, 1950 saw the beginning of another great assault on the Himalayas.

In 1950 a French group, led by Maurice Herzog, scaled Annapurna (26,502 feet), in central Nepal, the first "eight-thousander" (a mountain over 8,000 meters high—there are 14 in the Himalayan chain, none anywhere else) ever to be climbed, despite 22 previous tries. After leaving their supply base on the Pokhara plateau, halfway from the railhead to the mountain, the climbers reported their daily progress by radio. The whole world followed their successes and setbacks. Mountaineers everywhere counted the weeks, the days, the hours, before the monsoons were due to strike. The climbers and porters struggled up and down the mountainside in relays, under 40-pound loads, carrying the food, tents, sleeping bags, stoves, clothing and all the other gear necessary to establish and maintain the chain of camps on the glacier and the upper slopes. Storms swept the peak again and again, preventing an assault. Avalanches and accidents presented additional difficulties. Then, on June 2, came a brief break in the bad weather. Herzog himself, and Louis Lachenal, reached the summit. However, Herzog lost his gloves while taking pictures—he was suffering severely from lack of oxygen and hardly knew what he was doing—and the descent turned into pure nightmare. A storm hit, and Herzog nearly died of exposure; at one point he was thrown 500 feet by an avalanche. Back at Camp II he underwent the most excruciating antifrostbite injections, then had to be carried on a litter for almost four weeks, delirious and close to death, down through the passes and valleys back to civilization. On the way, Dr. Oudot, the team's physician, was forced to amputate all his fingers and toes. Louis Lachenal, also severely frostbitten, lost only his toes.

There remained the tallest mountain of them all, brutal Everest, half a mile higher than Annapurna, a killer which had resisted more than 30 years of desperate struggle to conquer it. Everest was discovered in 1852, when a clerk of the British Trigonometrical Survey in India, working on some sightings made from near the Indian border four years earlier, found to his surprise that "Peak XV," on the distant Nepal-Tibet border and almost hidden behind nearer and apparently taller mountains, was almost 1,000 feet higher than any other peak surveyed. Named for a previous Surveyor-General, Sir George Everest, it immediately became the object of mountaineers' thought and study. However, it was not until 1921 that a British party, with Tibetan permission, explored the northern approaches to the mountain and found a route up the Rongbuk Glacier. From there, George Leigh-Mallory, one of the finest climbers then living, with two companions and several porters, reached the North Col, a saddle well up the mountain's northeast ridge, 23,000 feet above sea level, which promised to give access to the upper slopes and the summit.

The next year Mallory went back with a large party including 13 Englishmen and more than 150 porters. He retraced his route to the North Col, and from there established a small camp at 25,000 feet, higher than man had ever climbed before. Mallory and two companions then tried to go on to the top, but found that they were so weakened by lack of oxygen that they could only advance 300 feet an hour. They abandoned the climb at 27,000 feet. After Mallory's failure, two other English climbers, Geoffrey Bruce and George Finch, and a Gurkha soldier, Tejbir, made an attempt. Using oxygen equipment—primitive gear which was both heavy and inefficient—they reached 27,235 feet, but there had to stop, tantalized at being close enough to see individual stones just short of the summit. The oxygen, which the Sherpas laughingly called "English air," although of little use on the climb, saved their lives when it kept them from freezing to death in a windstorm.

Despite his second failure, Mallory refused to give up and, having reorganized at a lower camp, he once more attacked the upper slopes, but was stopped by an avalanche that killed seven porters and almost swept away the whole party.

AFTER two years of waiting and organizing, the English again set out to climb Everest in 1924. The expedition of almost 300 men included a number from the earlier efforts, notably Mallory, who seems to have believed that it was his fate to conquer Everest or die in the attempt. Such is the difficulty of operating in the Himalayan peaks that even the experience gained in 1921 and 1922 was of small use in 1924. The party, excellently organized and manned, still had a number of near-fatal accidents and was driven back to base camp by the weather. But still the men persevered and, on a third try, established the fifth of a series of tiny temporary camps at 25,300 feet. After being forced to retreat once more by the porters' fear of a storm, the climbers set up Camp VI at 26,800. From there, Edward Norton and Theodore Somervell, two strong climbers, attempted the summit on June 4. Despite the fact that Norton was seeing double from lack of oxygen and Somervell coughed so badly he was in danger of choking, they crossed the "yellow band," a stratum of sandstone which lies between 27,000 and 28,000 feet and which previous climbers had clearly seen but never reached. At 28,000 Somervell was forced to quit, but Norton went on over another 126 feet of slippery, tilelike shale. That was all he could manage; he too had to stop.

After these reverses it began to seem that Everest was a peak that could not be climbed, a giant, malevolent deity determined to defeat

RAPPELLING is a method used by mountaineers to get down steep rock or ice quickly and safely. A rope is doubled around a pinnacle or rock, or through a "piton." The climber then puts the doubled rope around a thigh, up across his chest and over the opposite shoulder. The friction of the rope around the climber's body enables him to control the rate of descent easily with his free hand. Arriving at the bottom, he disentangles himself and pulls the rope free to be used again.

man's best attempts. It was just too high, its weather too violent and unpredictable, its last 2,000 feet too treacherous. But Mallory would not give up. He determined to have one more try before the monsoon struck. He was joined by Andrew Irvine, a strong and enthusiastic if not very skilled young climber. After a day of preparation, Mallory and Irvine set out for Camp V on June 6, reached the next camp on the 7th, and on June 8 went for the top. N. E. Odell, who was on his way up to Camp VI as their "support," sighted them as they crept up a rocky ridge just below the last pyramid of the summit. They were "going strong for the top" but they were behind schedule; it was dangerously late in the day for them to be only that high if they expected to reach the summit and get down before dark. As Odell watched them, Mallory and Irvine disappeared in a mist.

That was the last anyone ever saw of either man. Odell, who retreated to Camp IV on the night of the 8th, made a heroic effort in the next two days to find them, going back up to Camp V with two Sherpas and on to Camp VI alone, and beyond that, but he saw no sign of life, no indication that the men had made it back to either camp. The fate of Mallory and Irvine has haunted mountaineers since. Did they reach the top? Did Mallory, despite his experience, climb too long, too late, and become lost in the dark? A night in the open on Everest, with howling winds and temperatures of 50 below zero, would surely have been fatal. A rusted ice ax belonging to one of the two men was found nine years later at about 28,000 feet by the next Everest expedition, but when it was dropped and under what circumstances no one could tell.

MALLORY's efforts were followed by three massive assaults in the 1930s. None succeeded. Everest was still unconquered after nearly two decades of effort. Seven men had reached 28,100 feet; none, with the possible exception of Mallory and Irvine, had gone any higher. Some of the climbers believed there was an invisible barrier at that height, that nobody ever would climb above it. At least one of them looked back on Everest as a mountain of "ferocious malignity."

Then World War II came, the Tibetan border was closed and has not been opened since. However, Nepal did open its borders to climbing expeditions, and those who wished to attempt Everest were confronted by a new problem. The part of Everest that lies in Nepal is the south face of the mountain which had never been climbed and which was considered by the few explorers and mountaineers who had seen it to be unscalable. Thus it was first necessary to map and explore the region. This was done in 1950 by Dr. Charles S. Houston, an American expert on altitude and acclimatization, and in 1951 by a great British Everester of the 1930s, Eric Shipton. The following year the Swiss made two attempts at the peak itself, one in the spring and one in the fall. Neither succeeded.

In 1953 the British decided to have another crack, with a party under the leadership of Colonel John Hunt. This was the most elaborate climbing expedition ever mounted. The climbers spent much more time than usual in acclimatizing themselves to the high altitude and then labored up the mountain's southwest face with five tons of equipment, much of it specially designed for the expedition. It took 362 porters to carry all these boxes from the supply base at Darjeeling in northeastern India. For more than 150 weary miles they trudged with their loads, up over passes 10,000 feet high, and down through hot, humid valleys barely 4,000 feet above sea level. Thirty-four experienced Sherpas came along to help when the glaciers were reached and the mountaineers began establishing their camps on the mountainside, each a little higher than the last. When the final assault was made, oxygen was used more extensively than ever before, both in climbing during the day and at night so that the user would not feel suffocated and be unable to sleep.

The last movement of this assault was conceived as a leapfrog operation. Two climbers, Tom Bourdillon and R. C. Evans, were to try first, leaving from a small camp some 3,300 feet below the summit, the eighth in a line strung out up the mountain's slope. Their support party, which included Colonel Hunt and several "tigers," as the high-climbing Sherpa porters were called, was to carry oxygen bottles and other supplies a little farther to Camp IX, which was to be simply the highest spot they could reach carrying heavy loads. In the event that Bourdillon and Evans failed, Edmund Hillary, a six-foot-three-inch New Zealander, and Tenzing Norgay, perhaps the most famous of the Sherpa tigers, were to proceed to Camp IX, rest overnight and then make the ultimate attempt.

Bourdillon and Evans did, in fact, fail, although they got within about 300 feet of the summit and reached a greater altitude than any climbers before them. Sick with exhaustion and disappointment, they still managed to give Hillary and Tenzing a minute description of what they would find after they had scaled the south summit which, from their perspective, hid the true summit from view. After having had to huddle in their tents at Camp VIII for an extra day and night because of a severe storm, Hillary and Tenzing, with their support party, proceeded to a height of 27,900 feet and established Camp IX. The support party left and the two men spent the night alone. The next day, May 29, they set out on their famous journey. They passed the place where, almost exactly a year earlier, Tenzing and Raymond Lambert had had to turn back, past the place where Bourdillon and Evans had been forced to retreat, and finally, past the south summit, over a last steep cliff, and on up the last ridges to the top. Everest was conquered. Hillary and Tenzing, despite their overwhelming elation, managed to take a number of photographs and, mindful of all those before them who had tried and failed, searched for traces of Mallory and Irvine. Then they descended and the whole party began its retreat to the glacier. Word of their successful ascent was flashed by radio to London on the eve of the coronation of Elizabeth II. Hillary and Colonel Hunt were both knighted by the new queen.

I F the ascent of Everest was the climax of Himalayan climbing, it was followed, against all laws of drama, by half a dozen other climaxes. Climbers from several nations continued the assault on the eight-thousanders and on a number of lesser peaks. The most dramatic of these post-Everest climbs were those on Nanga Parbat, Mount Godwin Austen and Kanchenjunga. The latter two are, after Everest, the tallest mountains in the world, and all three have been called more difficult than Everest. But they were all successfully scaled between 1953 and 1955 by German, Italian and English expeditions. Lhotse, Everest's sister peak and the fourth highest of all, was climbed by a Swiss expedition that also put men on top of

Everest twice in two days. A number of other Himalayan giants which had resisted all previous efforts also capitulated.

But mountaineering in the 1920s, Thirties and Fifties was not confined to the Himalayas. Many daring ascents were made elsewhere in the world, especially in the Alps and the Dolomites, where climbers tried ever more difficult routes up peaks long since climbed by their easier slopes. This kind of mountaineering, in which the emphasis was not on what mountain was ascended, but *how*, on the art of the matter rather than just altitude, had been going on since Whymper's time. Its greatest proponent had been an Englishman named A. F. Mummery, who climbed in the last decades of the 19th Century and who invented many of the techniques of modern climbing. Mummery became legendary among Alpinists for his climbs up the "impossible" rock spires which rise near Mont Blanc and Chamonix. The years between the two world wars saw a great deal of increasingly daring climbing. It ultimately led to a spirit of conquer-or-die known as the "cult of danger," which was unfortunately typical of a good deal of the climbing in these decades and especially of some German and Italian climbers who were spurred by intense nationalistic feelings. Climbing for the glory of the fatherland, for *Führer* or *Duce*, many tried rock faces beyond their skill, or anybody's skill, and fell to their deaths. The number of fatal accidents suffered in the Alps reached 400 in some years, a grotesque slaughter, but appropriate, perhaps, to a grotesque decade.

THE climax of this mania came in 1936, when two German and two Austrian youths tried to scale the face of the Eigerwand, a mile-high precipice near the Jungfrau. Many had tried to climb it before, none had succeeded, and almost every party that had made the attempt had lost at least one climber. As people watched through telescopes from the porch of a nearby hotel, the four young men crept upward with agonizing slowness. They spent two nights standing upright, lashed to the rock with ropes. On the second night a storm enveloped the mountain and everyone expected them to be blown away, but on the third morning they could still be seen. By this time the young men must have known it was hopeless and they started down. But, weakened as they were from exposure, that was impossible now. They just clung to the rock, motionless. Four guides banded together and tried to go to the rescue. But before they could get into a position to lower ropes, one of the young men lost his grip and plunged downward. The falling man's rope, getting twisted, nearly wrenched the head off one of his companions and a third was dragged downward and smashed against the rock face. The last young man cut the rope that bound him to these two corpses—the first to fall had gone all the way to the bottom—and almost managed to work his way to the guides, but then he too lost his hold and fell to his death.

Such excesses were not common elsewhere, and a great deal of healthy climbing was done in the Tetons, the best climbing mountains in the United States, in the Coast Range in British Columbia, in the Andes, in the New Zealand Alps, and even in Japan. Mountaineering clinics have been established on every continent. More and more people are climbing, fascinated, as all men must be, by the great mountains of our earth; and drawn also by the satisfaction any man must feel who has conquered a formidable natural obstacle through human ingenuity and courage.

THE MATTERHORN TOWERS 5,000 FEET ABOVE A SWISS VALLEY. THE FIRST ASCENT WAS MADE UP THE RIDGE IN THE FOREGROUND

Men against Mountains

Lofty and beautiful peaks like the Matterhorn have always awed and fascinated man. Only in modern times, however, has he felt the urge to climb them, only during the last century has he made repeated assaults on the most formidable. One by one they have yielded. Today almost all of the highest have been scaled, 11 of them, including Everest, in the decade 1950-1960.

A VISION OF CROSSES is seen by Whymper shortly after the accident. It was actually a fogbow, an optical effect often seen on mountains when the sun strikes clouds.

WHYMPER IN 1865

DANGEROUS FALL OF ROCK narrowly misses Whymper on the Matterhorn. This drawing and the one at top are two of the many Whymper made of his own Alpine adventures.

Victory and Death on the Matterhorn

When the passion for mountaineering suddenly flamed in the 19th Century, the Alps were the principal range to which climbers turned their attention. One after another the great peaks were climbed. But the Matterhorn, whose height and beauty made it the goal of almost every pioneer Alpinist, resisted all attempts. One man more than any other coveted the first ascent. He was Edward Whymper, an artist who had been sent to the Alps by a London publisher to make sketches and had become an ardent climber.

On his eighth attempt, in 1865, Whymper did reach the Matterhorn's summit, but as he and his party descended, there occurred the most famous of all Alpine disasters. One of Whymper's companions slipped and knocked over another. As these two fell they dislodged two more. The rope snapped and all four perished on the rocks below. This accident prompted a public outcry and many, including Queen Victoria, suggested mountaineering be outlawed. But it did not diminish the ardor of confirmed enthusiasts, or even retard the spread of Alpine fever.

DISASTER FOLLOWS VICTORY as four members of Whymper's party plunge to their deaths (*opposite*). This engraving was made by the 19th Century artist, Gustave Doré.

After Whymper: Ladies and Dogs

After the pioneering ascents of the 1860s, climbing in the Alps became increasingly popular. Even ladies took it up, some hesitantly and demurely, some—like Annie Peck—with fiery zeal. The subject's first great scholar appeared in the person of the Reverend W.A.B. Coolidge, who made 1,700 expeditions and wrote authoritatively of every Alpine pass and peak. At the same time great climbers like Alfred Mummery were developing many of the tools and techniques used since to bridge chasms and ascend near-vertical faces of ice, snow or rock (*see next pages*).

A HIGH-CLIMBING DOG named Tschingel, companion of W.A.B. Coolidge on 66 major ascents, holds all Alpine records for dogs.

FIRST AMERICAN WOMAN to climb the Matterhorn, Annie Smith Peck wears full regalia for her photograph. A schoolteacher, she climbed for nearly 40 years, stopped at 82.

LONG-SKIRTED LADIES take a guided outing on a glacier. Thousands of tourists made such modest excursions in the 1880s and Nineties, when the Alps became the fashion.

DANGEROUS SNOW CONDITIONS occur either when the slope is steep and icy, or where movement may start an avalanche. On the Eiger's North Wall in Switzerland (*opposite*), three climbers inch their way across an ice face where teamwork is vital. The men are roped together, the leader cuts steps in the ice, and only one man moves at a time.

EASY SNOW CONDITIONS are provided by a strip of old packed snow running up a ridge on Alaska's Mount Bertha. This was Mount Bertha's first ascent; the climbers worked their way up this snow tongue in preference to the more hazardous slippery rock. But climbers must watch for wavelike snow overhangs on ridges—they may fall through them.

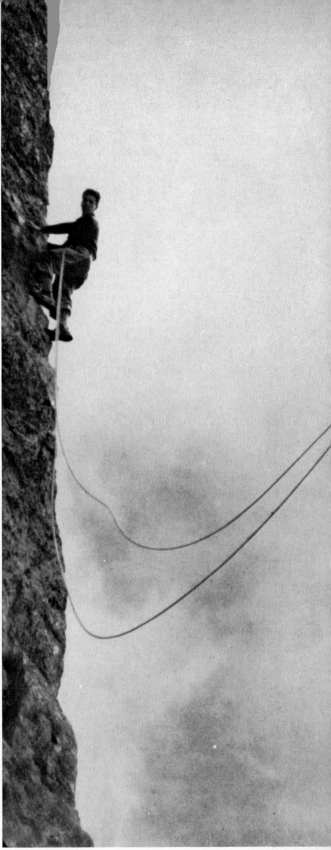

A TYROLEAN TRAVERSE is rigged by two climbers (*above*) high among the needles of Chamonix, granite spires which have fascinated many mountaineers.

RAPPELLING down a needle (*left*), an Alpinist plays out rope he has looped around one shoulder and under his hips. This is a quick, safe method of descent.

This traverse is a bridge made of rope which will loop the needle on the right and then be secured to *pitons*, iron spikes, driven in the rock face at left.

A CHIMNEY allows a climber to inch upward by pushing out with both feet (*right*). This man got around the stone wedged above him with *pitons* and rope.

Assault on Devils Tower

The fluted, nearly vertical sides of Devils Tower, a pillar of volcanic stone in Wyoming, appear murderous. But the Tower is not that forbidding. There are cracks which provide handholds, chimneys up which a climber can inch his way and outcrops which will hold ropes. Using these aids, dozens of climbers scaled the Tower during one week in 1956 without a single accident. This mass assault took place on the 50th anniversary of the Tower's being made a national monument, and more than 17 climbing clubs from all over the country sent teams. Most successful were those from the Army's Fort Carson Mountain Training Command. They worked out several new routes and one Army team made it to the top twice in one day, establishing on its second try a record of one hour and 28 minutes.

LIKE A GIGANTIC STUMP, Devils Tower rises abruptly 865 feet above its base in Wyoming. It is the hard core of a volcano whose softer slopes have long since eroded away.

TWO ARMY CLIMBERS in white (*opposite*) pioneer a difficult route up the side of Devils Tower. They worked their way up by ropes attached to spikes driven into the rock face.

SUCCESSFUL CLIMBERS STAND ON THE 275-FOOT-WIDE TOP OF THE TOWER. A HELICOPTER SUPPLIED SOME WHO CAMPED THERE

Fifty Famous Mountains

Here are 50 of the tallest, most important, or most famous mountains of the world, grouped and colored according to the regions in which they are located. The dates in the parentheses under their names are those of the earliest recorded ascents; question marks indicate that the date of the first ascent is unknown. The altitudes of these peaks, the nationalities of the men who first climbed them and other details of their histories are given in the Appendix, page 186.

30,000

28,000

26,000

24 000

22,000

20,000

18,000

16,000

14 000

12,000

10 000

8,000

6,000

4,000

2,000

SEA LEVEL

MCKINLEY
(1913)

ACONCAGUA
(1897)

CHIMBORAZO
(1880)

LOGAN
(1925)

COTOPAXI
(1872)

CITLALTEPETL
(1848)

KILIMANJARO
(1889)

ELBRUS
(1868)

POPOCATEPETL
(c. 1523)

KENYA
(1899)

VINSON MASSIF
(unscaled)

PIKES PEAK
(1820)

MARGHERITA
(1906)

MONT BLANC
(1786)

RAINIER
(1870)

WHITNEY
(1873)

MATTERHORN
(1865)

ELBERT
(?)

TOUBKAL
(1923)

GRAND TETON
(1898)

ETNA
(?)

OLYMPUS
(?)

GUNNBJORN
(1935)

WASHINGTON
(1642)

VESUVIUS
(?)

POLES   NORTH & SOUTH AMERICA   AFRICA   EUROPE

Logistics of the Remote Peaks

The great peaks of the Himalayas and the Karakoram lie many miles from the nearest railhead, airport or even road. All food, clothing and other gear for an assault must be carried on the backs of men, amazingly hardy Sherpa and Balti porters who can tote 250-pound loads day after day over impossibly rough terrain. The 1958 Italian expedition to Gasherbrum IV in the Karakoram employed 438 Baltis to carry supplies 137 miles across rock, river and glacier to the mountain's foot. Most famous are the Sherpas of Nepal, who have made a specialty of high porterage. Many have earned the title of "tiger" by carrying loads to the highest camps. A Sherpa, Tenzing Norgay, was one of the first two men to conquer Everest.

CARRYING A MAN, a porter crosses an icy stream high in the rocky uplands of the Karakoram. The feet of these mountain men are so tough they can walk barefoot on snow.

BALTI PORTERS rest against their heavy packs (*opposite*). They can carry such loads because their tribe has transported trading goods through these mountains for centuries.

PAYDAY FOR A PORTER comes at expedition's end. The wages of regular porters vary between $1.20 and two dollars a day, but high-climbing Sherpas normally get more.

Precipices, Storms and Deadly Cold

When an expedition has struggled to the base of a great mountain, it faces the most extreme climbing conditions in the world. Bitter cold, thin air, treacherous faces of rock or snow make it impossible for climbers to move upward more than a few hundred yards a day. A series of camps must be established and stocked, each within a day's climb of the next. In the advance camps, gales nightly threaten to blow the tents off the ledges on which they perch, snow sifts in at every crevice, and often the cold and wind are so intense the men cannot leave their cramped quarters for two days at a time.

FIVE MILES HIGH, a climber in Kashmir rounds a steep ridge. A slip would send him hurtling 7,000 feet to the glacier below. At such heights lack of oxygen weakens men and makes the climbing especially hazardous.

DIGGING OUT an advance camp (*left*) after a three-day storm, a climber tries to get the snow off his tent. A ripped tent at these altitudes, where the temperature may drop to 50 degrees below zero, can be a fatal catastrophe.

UNDER 60-POUND LOADS, INCLUDING OXYGEN BOTTLES, HILLARY AND TENZING CLIMB DOGGEDLY TOWARD THE FINAL ASSAULT CAMP

WITH ENDLESS CUPS OF TEA, Tenzing and Hillary soothe their parched throats as they rest after the ascent. Hillary was so tired he felt it was all happening to someone else.

The Highest of All

The first men to reach the summit of Everest, the world's highest mountain, were Edmund Hillary, a tall New Zealander, and Tenzing Norgay, a Sherpa porter who had performed so brilliantly on previous expeditions that he was made a full-fledged climber. After a cold, uncomfortable night at Camp IX—one small tent on a ledge at 27,900 feet—Hillary and Tenzing started for the top at dawn on May 29, 1953. Climbing carefully and using oxygen, they struggled up the razor-backed South Ridge. At 11:30 a.m. the ridge suddenly ran level and they realized that the mountain which had defeated seven major expeditions had at last been climbed.

AT THE GREAT MOMENT, Tenzing (*opposite*) holds up flags of the U.N., Britain, Nepal and India. While Hillary took other pictures, Tenzing buried gifts for his Buddhist gods.

Appendix

Listed below are mountains celebrated for their height, for the difficulties they have presented mountaineers or for their impact on human life. A few, like Vesuvius and Pelée, are volcanoes that have wiped out entire cities. Others, like Etna, Olympus and Ararat, were objects of religious veneration for the people living nearby at the dawn of history. Still others are holy mountains today, Fujiyama to the people of Japan, Sri Pada to all three of the major Asian faiths—Mohammedan, Buddhist and Hindu —that flourish in Ceylon. The Alps of Europe and the towering peaks of the central Asian plateau are, of course, best known as the scenes of great mountaineering adventures.

PEAK AND LOCATION	ALTITUDE	OTHER PERTINENT FACTS
North America		
McKinley, Alaska	20,320	Highest on continent, base-to-peak rise 18,500. First ascent 1913 (U.S.)
Logan, Canada	19,850	Second highest on continent. First ascent 1925 (joint Canadian-U.S. party)
Citlaltepetl (Orizaba), Mexico	18,696	Snow-covered volcanic peak. First ascent 1848 (French)
Popocatepetl, Mexico	17,887	Sacred Aztec peak profaned by conquistadors who climbed it in search of sulphur for gunpowder. Long dormant, it began to smoke again in 1965.
Blackburn, Alaska	16,523	First major North American climb led by a woman (Dora Keen, U.S., 1912)
Whitney, California	14,495	Until annexation of Alaska, highest in U.S. First ascent 1873 (U.S.)
Elbert, Colorado	14,431	First ascent claimed in 1847 (U.S.), but previously climbed by trappers and Indians
Rainier, Washington	14,410	Volcanic peak bearing 26 glaciers. First ascent 1870 (U.S.)
Pikes Peak, Colorado	14,110	First recorded ascent 1820 (U.S.). Now has auto road to summit
Grand Teton, Wyoming	13,766	From 1810 to 1840 resort of trappers and "mountain men." First ascent 1898 (U.S.)
Gunnbjörn, Greenland	12,139	Highest Arctic peak. First ascent 1935 (British)
Washington, New Hampshire	6,288	First peak in U.S. scaled by a white man (Darby Field, New Hampshire, 1642)
Pelée, Martinique	5,243	Wiped out entire city of St. Pierre (30,000 killed) in 1902 eruption
South America		
Aconcagua, Argentina	22,834	World's longest drop, over nine miles from summit to ocean bottom (Peru-Chile Trench) 100 miles away. First ascent 1897 (British)
Huascarán, Peru	22,205	First major peak climbed by a woman (Annie S. Peck, U.S., 1908)
Chimborazo, Ecuador	20,577	Attempted 1802 by German explorer Humboldt, scaled 1880 by Whymper (British)
Cotopaxi, Ecuador	19,344	Active volcano. Attempted 1802 by Humboldt. First ascent 1872 (German)
Europe		
Elbrus, U.S.S.R.	18,468	Highest on continent. First ascent 1868 (British)
Mont Blanc, France	15,781	Highest in the Alps. First ascent 1786 (French)
Matterhorn, Switzerland	14,685	Resisted many assaults, finally scaled by Whymper in 1865
Wetterhorn, Switzerland	12,166	Climbed by British in 1854, marks start of "golden age" of mountaineering
Etna, Italy	10,868	Highest active volcano in Europe; more than 260 recorded eruptions in 2,500 years
Olympus, Greece	9,550	Abode of the gods of Greek mythology
Vesuvius, Italy	3,842	Only active volcano on European mainland. Destroyed Pompeii in A.D. 79
Africa		
Kilimanjaro, Tanganyika	19,340	Extinct volcano. First ascent 1889 (German)
Kenya, Kenya	17,040	Extinct volcanic cone, almost directly on equator. First ascent 1899 (British)
Margherita, The Congo	16,821	Highest peak of the Ruwenzori. First ascent 1906 (Italian)
Toubkal, Morocco	13,661	Highest in North Africa. First ascent 1923 (French)
Asia		
Everest, Nepal	29,028	Highest in the world. First ascent 1953 (British-Sherpa party)
K2 (Godwin Austen), Kashmir	28,250	Second highest in world. First ascent 1954 (Italian)
Kanchenjunga, Sikkim	28,168	First ascent 1955 (British)
Lhotse, Nepal	27,890	First ascent 1956 (Swiss)
Makalu, Nepal	27,790	First ascent 1955 (French)
Cho Oyu, Nepal	26,867	First ascent 1954 (Austrian). All-woman attempt in 1959 ended in death of four
Dhaulagiri, Nepal	26,810	First ascent 1960 (Swiss). Two died in previous attempts
Nanga Parbat, Jammu-Kashmir	26,660	First ascent 1953 (German-Austrian team). In previous attempts, 29 were killed
Manaslu, Nepal	26,657	First ascent 1956 (Japanese). Buddhist leader considered ascent a pilgrimage
Annapurna, Nepal	26,502	First "eight-thousander" conquered; scaled 1950 (French)
Gasherbrum, Jammu-Kashmir	26,470	First ascent 1958 (U.S.)
Broad Peak, Jammu-Kashmir	26,414	First ascent 1957 (Austrian)
Gosainthan, Tibet	26,291	Unscaled; lies in a little-known section of Nepal-Tibet Himalayan range
Tirich Mir, Pakistan	25,426	Highest in the Hindu Kush. First ascent 1950 (Norwegian)
Mount Communism, U.S.S.R.	24,590	Formerly called Stalin Peak. First ascent 1933 (Soviet)
Mustagh Tower, Jammu-Kashmir	23,860	First ascent 1956 (British)
Tengri Khan, U.S.S.R.-China	22,940	First ascent 1931 (Japanese)
Ararat, Turkey	16,946	Extinct volcano. Reputed resting place of Noah's Ark. First ascent 1829 (German)

PEAK AND LOCATION	ALTITUDE	OTHER PERTINENT FACTS
Carstensz, West Irian, New Guinea	16,503	Highest island-mountain peak in the world. First ascent 1936 (Netherlands)
Kinabalu, Borneo	13,455	First ascent unrecorded
Fujiyama, Japan	12,389	Shintoist sacred mountain, highest in Japan. Dormant volcano, last eruption 1707
Sri Pada (Adam's Peak), Ceylon	7,360	Sacred mountain venerated by Buddhists, Moslems and Hindus
Antarctica, Australia and Oceania		
Vinson Massif, Antarctica	16,860	Highest known Antarctic peak. First ascent 1966 (U.S.)
Mauna Kea, Hawaii	13,796	Active volcano, highest unbroken base-to-peak rise in the world (32,000 ft. from ocean bed)
Cook, New Zealand	12,349	Highest peak in Dominion. First ascent 1894 (New Zealand)
Kosciusko, Australia	7,316	Highest peak on continent. First ascent unrecorded

Picture Credits
Credits for pictures from left to right are separated by commas, top to bottom by dashes.

Cover: Ray Atkeson. 8: Minor White from Gamma. 12: Drawing by Frances W. Zweifel. 14: Drawing by Adolph E. Brotman. 15: Drawing by Adolph E. Brotman. 17: Georgia Engelhard from Monkmeyer Press Photos. 18, 19: Bob and Ira Spring. 20, 21: Dmitri Kessel. 22: Charles E. Rotkin from Photography for Industry. 23: Swiss National Tourist Office, Bob and Ira Spring. 24, 25: Swissair. 26: Georgia Engelhard from Monkmeyer Press Photos. 27: A. Klopfenstein from Swiss National Tourist Office. 28, 29: left Swissair; center Meerkamper from Monkmeyer Press Photos—Monkmeyer Press Photos; right Swissair. 30: NBC Newsreel from United Press International except top right United Press International. 31: N. R. Farbman. 32: Bradford Washburn. 34, 35: Drawings by Matt Greene. 36: Drawings by Mark A. Binn. 38: Drawings by Adolph E. Brotman. 41: William A. Garnett. 42: Ansel Adams from the book *This Is the American Earth* published by Sierra Club. 43: Ray Atkeson. 44, 45: Painting by Ray Pioch. 46, 47: Painting by Kenneth S. Fagg. 48, 49: Ray Atkeson, Andreas Feininger (2)—George Silk. 50, 51: Ray Atkeson. 52: Juan Guzman. 54: Drawings by Adolph E. Brotman. 57: Drawings by Matt Greene. 58: Drawing by Kenneth Gosner. 61: Drawings by Mark A. Binn. 63: Brown Brothers. 64, 65: Culver Pictures—courtesy Museo Nazionale, Giovanni Vetti, David Lees. 66: Courtesy American Museum of Natural History. 67: Courtesy American Museum of Natural History—Brown Brothers. 68: R. W. Decker. 69: Herb Taylor from Pix. 70, 71: Robert Wenkam, Camera Hawaii from Alpha Photo Associates, Inc. 72, 73: Jerry Y. Chong from Camera Hawaii. 74, 75: N. R. Farbman except top right Robert Wenkam. 76: Ralph Crane. 77: Oliver E. Allen. 78: C. W. Close from Shostal. 79: Haroun Tazieff. 80: Klopfenstein-Adelboden. 82: Drawing by Adolph E. Brotman. 84 through 89: Drawings by Frances W. Zweifel. 91: O. P. Pearson. 92, 93: Eliot Elisofon—Andreas Feininger, R. Daubenmire. 94: Drawing by Kenneth Gosner. 95: Eliot Elisofon. 96: Emil Schulthess from Black Star—Eliot Elisofon. 97: Emil Schulthess from Black Star. 98, 99: Eliot Elisofon. 100, 101: Emil Schulthess from Black Star. 102: Dr. William Osburn—Georgia Engelhard from Monkmeyer Press Photos. 103: Baron Hans von Meiss-Teuffen from Photo Researchers, Inc., Dmitri Kessel—Harold Malde. 104, 105: Eliot Porter. 106: A. Y. Owen. 108, 109: Drawings by Frances W. Zweifel. 111: Drawing by Kenneth Gosner. 112: Drawings by Frances W. Zweifel. 115: Drawing by Kenneth Gosner. 117: R. Van Nostrand from National Audubon Society. 118: Wilford L. Miller from National Audubon Society. 119: left courtesy American Museum of Natural History; right Cleveland P. Grant. 120, 121: Fritz Siedel. 122, 123: A. Y. Owen, Roger Tory Peterson. 124: George Silk. 125: Ed Park—Eliot Porter. 126, 127: Allan D. Cruickshank from National Audubon Society, George Silk. 128: Burt Glinn from Magnum. 131: Chart by Matt Greene. 132: Drawing by Adolph E. Brotman. 135: Drawing by Frances W. Zweifel. 139: Dmitri Kessel. 140, 141: Eliot Elisofon except top right Barry C. Bishop copyright World Book Encyclopedia. 142: Eliot Elisofon. 143: John Collier from Gamma—Eliot Elisofon. 144: Frank J. Scherschel. 145: Dmitri Kessel. 146, 147: Frank J. Scherschel except bottom left Dmitri Kessel. 148, 149: Douglas Scott. 150: Fosco Maraini for Monkmeyer Press Photos. 151: Tse Ten-Tashi. 152: Douglas Scott. 153: C. S. Cutting—Tse Ten-Tashi. 154, 155: Mrs. Homai Vyarawalla, C. S. Cutting. 156: Riccardo Cassin. 159, 161: Drawings by Mark A. Binn. 164: Drawing by Matt Greene. 167: Ewing Galloway. 168: top left Müller from Swiss National Tourist Office; bottom from *Scrambles Amongst the Alps* published by John Murray. 169: Culver Pictures. 170: European Picture Service. 171: Ronald W. Clark—Picture Post Library from Black Star. 172: Copyright Hiebeler. 173: Bradford Washburn. 174, 175: Olaf Soot, Howard Friedman for SPORTS ILLUSTRATED, Bob and Ira Spring. 176, 177: Carl Iwasaki. 178, 179: Painting by Bob Riley. 180: Fosco Maraini from Monkmeyer Press Photos. 181: Dr. Charles S. Houston—Fosco Maraini from Monkmeyer Press Photos. 182, 183: Dr. Charles S. Houston. 184, 185: Copyright Mount Everest Foundation.

Acknowledgments

The editors of this book are particularly indebted to William S. Osburn, Associate Director, Institute of Arctic and Alpine Research, University of Colorado, who read the entire book and criticized the chapters in his own area of study. The editors are also indebted to Charles H. Behre Jr., Professor of Economic Geology, Columbia University; Carleton S. Coon, Professor of Anthropology, University of Pennsylvania; Charles S. Houston, M.D., Aspen Clinic; Henry Sharp, Chairman of the Department of Geology and Geography, Barnard College; James Matthai, Geography Department, Teachers College, Columbia University; George Fielding Eliot; Grant W. Sharpe, Associate Professor of Forestry, University of Michigan; Bassett Maguire, Head Curator, New York Botanical Garden; Colin M. Turnbull, Associate Curator of African Ethnology, American Museum of Natural History; Walter Fairservis, Research Associate, Department of Anthropology, American Museum of Natural History; Guinevere C. Smith, Carnegie Institution of Washington; R. W. Decker, Assistant Professor of Geology, Dartmouth College; Sydney Anderson, Associate Curator of Mammalogy, American Museum of Natural History; R. F. Daubenmire, Professor of Botany, State College of Washington; J. Gordon Edwards, Professor of Entomology, San Jose State College; David J. Rogers, New York Botanical Garden; J. M. Thorington and the American Alpine Club; U.S. Coast and Geodetic Survey; American Geographic Society; and the National Audubon Society.

Bibliography

Geology and Geography

Atwood, Wallace W., *The Physiographic Provinces of North America.* Ginn, 1940.

Beiser, Arthur, *Our Earth.* E. P. Dutton, 1959.

Dunbar, Carl O., *Historical Geology* (2nd ed.). John Wiley & Sons, 1960.

Finch, Vernor C., Glenn T. Trewartha, Arthur H. Robinson and Edwin H. Hammond, *Elements of Geography.* McGraw-Hill, 1957.

Fitz Gerald, E. A., *The Highest Andes.* Scribner, 1899.

Flint, Richard Foster, *Glacial and Pleistocene Geology.* John Wiley & Sons, 1957.

Jacobs, J. A., R. D. Russell and J. T. Wilson, *Physics and Geology.* McGraw-Hill, 1959.

James, Preston E., *An Outline of Geography.* Ginn, 1943.

Lobeck, A. K., *Geomorphology.* McGraw-Hill, 1939.

Peattie, Roderick, ed., *The Sierra Nevada.* Vanguard, 1947.

Strahler, Arthur N., *Physical Geography.* John Wiley & Sons, 1960.

Von Engeln, O. D., and Kenneth E. Caster, *Geology.* McGraw-Hill, 1952.

Mountain Animal Life

Allee, W. C., Alfred E. Emerson, Orlando Park, Thomas Park and Karl P. Schmidt, *Principles of Animal Ecology* (rev. ed.). W. B. Saunders, 1949.

Anthony, H. E., *Field Book of North American Mammals.* G. P. Putnam's Sons, 1928.

Bourlière, François, *Mammals of the World.* Alfred Knopf, 1955.

* Colbert, Edwin H., *Evolution of the Vertebrates.* John Wiley & Sons, 1955.

Drimmer, Frederick, ed., *The Animal Kingdom* (3 vols.). Doubleday, 1954.

Gilliard, E. Thomas, *Living Birds of the World.* Doubleday, 1958.

Harrison, Hal H., *American Birds in Color.* William H. Wise, 1948.

Hesse, Richard, W. C. Allee and K. P. Schmidt, *Ecological Animal Geography* (2nd ed.). John Wiley & Sons, 1951.

Munro, G. C., *Birds of Hawaii.* Bridgeway Press, Japan, 1960.

† Olin, George, and Edward Bierly, *Mammals of the Southwest Mountains and Mesas.* Southwestern Monuments Association, 1961.

Sanderson, Ivan T., *Living Mammals of the World.* Hanover House, 1955.

Wallace, George J., *An Introduction to Ornithology.* Macmillan, 1955.

Young, J. Z., *The Life of Vertebrates.* Oxford University Press, 1952.

Mountain Plant Life

Dansereau, Pierre, *Biogeography.* Ronald Press, 1957.

Daubenmire, R. F., *Plants and Environment* (rev. ed.). John Wiley & Sons, 1959.

Dice, Lee R., *Natural Communities.* University of Michigan Press, 1952.

Lawrence, George H. M., *Taxonomy of Vascular Plants.* Macmillan, 1960.

Lemmon, R. S., and C. C. Johnson, *Wildflowers of North America.* Hanover House, 1961.

* McDougall, Walter, *Plants of the Yellowstone.* Yellowstone Library and Museum Association, 1956.

Moldenke, Harold N., *American Wild Flowers.* D. Van Nostrand, 1949.

Oosting, Henry J., *The Study of Plant Communities* (rev. ed.). W. H. Freeman, 1953.

Schimper, A.F.W., *Plant Geography upon a Physiological Basis.* Hafner, 1960.

Mountain People

Alexander, Robert J., *The Bolivian National Revolution.* Rutgers University Press, 1958.

Bell, Sir Charles Alfred, *Religion of Tibet.* Oxford University Press, 1931.

Bennett, Wendell C., and Junius B. Bird, *Andean Culture History.* American Museum of Natural History, 1960.

Bishop, R.N.W., *Unknown Nepal.* Luzac, London, 1952.

Bushnell, Geoffrey, *Peru.* Praeger, 1957.

Coon, Carleton S., *The Races of Europe.* Macmillan, 1939.

De Riencourt, Amaury, *Roof of the World.* Rinehart, 1950.

De Terra, Helmut, *Humboldt.* Alfred Knopf, 1955.

* Harrer, Heinrich, *Seven Years in Tibet.* E. P. Dutton, 1959.

Lackey, Earl E., and Esther S. Anderson, *Regions and Nations of the World.* D. Van Nostrand, 1953.

Leonard, Olen E., *Bolivia.* Scarecrow, 1952.

* Maraini, Fosco, *Secret Tibet.* Viking Press, 1952.

Moraes, Frank, *The Revolt in Tibet.* Macmillan, 1960.

Osborne, Harold, *Indians of the Andes.* Harvard University Press, 1952.

Shen, Tsung-lien, and Shen-chi Liu, *Tibet and the Tibetans.* Stanford University Press, 1953.

Stein, William W., *Hualcan: Life in the Highlands of Peru.* Cornell University Press, 1961.

Adventure and Exploration

Brown, Belmore, *The Conquest of Mount McKinley.* Houghton Mifflin, 1956.

Buhl, Hermann, *Lonely Challenge.* E. P. Dutton, 1956.

Burt, F. Allen, *The Story of Mount Washington.* Dartmouth University Press, 1960.

Douglas, William O., *Beyond the High Himalayas.* Doubleday, 1953.

Herzog, Maurice, *Annapurna: First Conquest of an 8,000-Meter Peak.* E. P. Dutton, 1952.

Hillary, Sir Edmund, *High Adventure.* E. P. Dutton, 1955.

Houston, Charles S., *K2, The Savage Mountain.* McGraw-Hill, 1954.

Hunt, Sir John, *The Conquest of Everest.* E. P. Dutton, 1954.

Lowe, George, *From Everest to the South Pole.* St. Martin's Press, 1961.

Lunn, Arnold, *A Century of Mountaineering, 1857-1957.* Macmillan, 1959.

Maraini, Fosco, *Karakoram.* Viking Press, 1961.

Tilman, Harold William, *Snow on the Equator.* Macmillan, 1938.

Ullman, James Ramsey, *Age of Mountaineering.* J. B. Lippincott, 1954.

Whymper, Edward, *Scrambles Amongst the Alps in the Years 1860-69* (rev. ed.). Transatlantic, 1960.

General

† Asimov, Isaac, *The Bloodstream: River of Life.* Collier Books, 1961.

* Bates, D. R., ed., *The Earth and Its Atmosphere.* John Wiley & Sons, 1957.

Brion, Marcel and E. Smith, *Pompeii and Herculaneum.* Crown, 1960.

Fuller, J.F.C., *A Military History of the Western World.* Funk and Wagnalls, 1954.

Gaussen, Henri, and Paul Barruel, *Montagnes.* Horizons de France, Paris, 1955.

Herzog, Maurice, ed., *La Montagne.* Librairie Larousse, Paris, 1956.

Lane, F. C., *The Story of Mountains.* Doubleday, 1951.

Morrill, Madge H., *John Muir, Protector of the Wilds.* Abingdon Press, 1957.

Pearsall, W. H., *Mountains and Moorlands.* Collins, London, 1960.

Robinson, M. L., *Runner of the Mountain Tops: the Life of Louis Agassiz.* Random House, 1939.

Simpson, George Gaylord, Colin S. Pittendrigh and Lewis H. Tiffany, *Life: An Introduction to Biology.* Harcourt, Brace, 1957.

Sitwell, Sacheverell, *Golden Wall and Mirador.* World, 1961.

Synge, Patrick, *Mountains of the Moon.* Lindsay Drummond, Ltd., London, 1937.

Ullman, James Ramsey, *The Other Side of the Mountain.* Carrick and Evans, 1938.

* Also available in paperback edition.

† Only available in paperback edition.

Index

Numerals in italics indicate a photograph or painting of the subject mentioned.

✕✕✕✕✕✕

Production Staff for Time Incorporated
John L. Hallenbeck (Vice President and Director of Production), Robert E. Foy and Caroline Ferri
Text photocomposed under the direction of Albert J. Dunn and Arthur J. Dunn